THE PANIC IN NEEDLE PARK

THE PANIC IN NEEDLE PARK

by James Mills

FARRAR, STRAUS AND GIROUX
NEW YORK

First printing, 1966

Published simultaneously in Canada by Ambassador Books, Ltd., Toronto
Printed in the United States of America
Designed by Betty Crumley

This story is both fiction and fact: fiction in that none of its characters ever existed exactly as described; fact in that none of the characters or events is an impossibility in the junkie world. Everything that happens here has happened many times, to individuals not unlike the characters described in this book.

c. 3

THE PANIC IN NEEDLE PARK

From legal poppy fields in Turkey, by camel across the sands of Syria to the not-so-legal laboratories in Lebanon, then by ship to southern France for final refining, back to Italy and, courtesy of the Mafia, to New York's docks and airports—heroin comes to Harlem. And from Harlem the drug moves swiftly through the city of New York, as efficiently and regularly as milk from New Jersey or fish from Fulton Street. As it moves, the illicit stream swells into pools from which addicts in various parts of the city draw their daily needs. Addicts—and the police—are as aware of the selling locations as the housewife is of her neighborhood shopping center.

In the rush and confusion at 96th Street and Broadway addicts gather on the corner to meet the pushers and buy their drugs—ignored by crowds of New Yorkers on their way to work. On the southwest corner of 82nd Street and Columbus Avenue, two blocks from Manhattan's Museum of Natural History and the expensive Central Park West apartments nearby, addicts spend thousands of dollars a day for heroin. In front of a drugstore at 47th Street and Seventh Avenue, within the chaotic glow of Times Square, unknowing tourists brush shoulder to shoulder with barbiturate addicts waiting stiff and zombielike for their connections. It's the same just two blocks south, among the honky-tonk bars and nightclubs, or down in Greenwich Village, where heroin and marijuana pass from hand to hand on the benches of Washington Square.

But occasionally—perhaps once a year—the stream of illegal drugs is partially dammed, usually at its European source, and then heroin grows scarce. At such times, addicts talk of "panic." The price of heroin goes up. The addicts must steal more, hustle more, look more desperately for good connections, settle for weaker drugs, get high less often. Some of the older ones, finding the hustle at last too great to bear, give up the habit completely and never return to drugs. Others, in the heightened frenzy of their search for heroin, step too far; and because they have stolen from the wrong man, or cheated a connection too often, or been driven to too great a recklessness, they disappear—some quietly and without a trace, some violently in the crack of gunfire and flash of red police lights.

No one talks of anything but the panic: what has caused it (the pushers have gone to Florida for the winter; ten tons of opium were seized in Turkey; politicians are getting scared and putting the heat on the gangsters), how it compares with other panics in other years (worse, much worse, than last year, but not anywhere near as bad as '62 —no panic could be as bad as the one in '62; in '62 junkies were kicking their habits in the streets, doorways in Harlem were littered with sick, vomiting junkies, hospitals were full, doctors' offices jammed), and when it will end—always the talk is about when it will end (Joe knows the top guy up in Harlem, man, and he says they got a shipment in yesterday. They're just waitin' for things to cool a little more, man, and then it'll break; Joe says it'll break tomorrow, maybe. Tomorrow, man. Boy, if it *don't* break tomorrow, I'll tell you, man, I don't know. I just *don't know.* This panic is somethin' else, man, somethin' *else*).

Today in New York no one has forgotten the panic of 1964. In late evening twilight on a Thursday in October of that year, two men dressed as hunters approached a red-roofed stone farmhouse in the countryside near Marseilles. One of the men, apparently wounded in an accident, lay across the shoulders of his companion. When the men were about twenty yards from the house, they called out for help. A young woman came to the door, opened it cautiously, and looked out. Instantly the man who had appeared injured slid from his friend's shoulders and both men charged through the door. One grabbed the startled woman's hand from a warning buzzer and the other headed for the stairs, followed by fifteen uniformed policemen who came running from clumps of trees near the house. On the second floor, they found five astonished Frenchmen surrounded by a roomful of laboratory equipment. Near them, stacked in sacks like potatoes, were bags containing 220 pounds of morphine base. In a corner of the room sat a broad pyramid of glassine bags filled with 220 pounds of pure heroin.

The heroin alone was enough to provide New York City's addicts with 4½ million shots, at a final retail price of $22½ million. It was the largest heroin seizure in history, and for French police it meant the end of months of laborious undercover work. For the laboratory's owner, a forty-nine-year-old Corsican named Joseph André Cesari, it meant a possible ten years in jail and a $1 million fine. And for the addicts in New York it meant the longest and worst panic almost any of them could remember—worse even than 1962. It was especially bad for two of them, a young man and woman named Robert Axel and Helen Reeves. This is the story of how they lived in the panic, and what became of them.

book one

Chapter 1

Four times a day, junkies like Bob and Helen are holed up with heroin. Faces desperate and intent, teeth pull tight the tourniquet, grimy fingers squeeze fluid into the bloodstream, and then—peace. With the shot, their problems vanish, and the world they cannot handle fades to leave them in solitary bliss. This is everything they live for; this is what heroin is all about.

Bob and Helen had much in common with other big-city junkies. When the panic began, Helen was twenty-three, Bob twenty-one. Both had broken the law before they started on heroin—she as a prostitute in Denver, he as a petty thief in New York. Helen was the first in her family to use illegal drugs; but Bob had one addicted brother. Helen was the daughter of an engineer, brought up in a pleasant middle-class neighborhood of Denver. Bob's father was a janitor in an office building, and found himself every few years moving from one New York tenement to another.

Both Bob and Helen had used many drugs, but they preferred heroin to all the rest, just as a gourmet prefers wine to beer. Both had been in jail (he eight times, she twice) and to hospitals (he five times, she once)—and had emerged each time to start their habits fresh. Helen's last arrest had been for selling heroin, and she was free on a three-year suspended sentence.

Bob and Helen had been together—sleeping wherever they could find a place to lie down—for two years. They used the same last name—in courts, jails, hospitals, hotels, she signed herself "Helen Axel"—but never got around to formal marriage ("We did get a blood test once," said Helen). Helen's earnings as a prostitute also supported Bob's habit, and he occasionally contributed a little money by breaking into parked cabs, in which drivers often leave coin changers.

Both Bob and Helen were at times all but overcome by revulsion for their habit and for the horrifying, unseen world it forced them into. "We are all animals," Helen said. "We are all animals in a world no one knows."

Chapter 2

No "square"—the addict's word for anyone who does not use drugs—can imagine the strength of heroin's hold. The addict will beg for it, walk miles for it, wait hours for it, con for it, stay up days and nights on end to pursue it, steal from those he has loved for it, risk death for it. It is his jealous lover, and his wrathful god.

The heroin addict is a very busy man. For those who would separate him from his heroin he has no use and no time. When he awakes in the morning, he reaches instantly for his "works"—eyedropper, needle ("spike," he calls it), and bottle top ("cooker"). He dissolves heroin in water in the cooker and injects the mixture. This is his "wake-up," a morning shot to hold off the anxiety and sickness of with-drawal and get him "straight" enough to start the day. If his habit is costing him $20 a day, and that is not a large habit by any means, he must now start out to steal at least $100 worth of goods, knowing that a fence will give him only one fifth the true value of his loot. When he has stolen something, he must haggle with his fence over the price. The argument seems interminable to him, for it has now been hours since his wake-up and he is getting nervous again, his eyes are watering and he is beginning to feel like a man coming down with a bad case of flu.

Finally he gets the money and begins his search for a connection. Not just any connection, but a connection who deals good quality stuff—"dynamite," not "garbage." Once the addict has bought his fix (has "copped" or "scored"), he is faced with the risky business of getting it to his cooker and into his arm without getting caught and "busted" (arrested). When he has finally injected the heroin (he calls it "shooting up," "taking off," "getting off"), he may or may not go on a "nod"—his eyelids heavy, his mind wandering pleasantly—depending on how much heroin his body has become accustomed to and how much actual heroin was in the powder he injected.

He hopes that the shot will be at least strong enough to make him straight for a few hours. He can judge immedi-ately the quality of the shot. If it is strong enough, he calms down, the flu feeling leaves, and he instantly begins looking for money for the next shot.

His adversaries in this continual quest are always the

police: the "narcos," "The Man." But he knows, though usually he will not admit it, that while the cops pursue him, the law itself, as it must finally be interpreted in court, is on his side, or at least on the side of his addiction. Stringent search and seizure laws make it tough for detectives to produce unshakable evidence against the addict and the pusher. Merely being an addict is not a crime in New York; he must have drugs or a hypodermic needle in his possession. Many addicts—especially pushers—wear a rubber band on their wrists (a dealer's band, some call it) which, if hooked properly around a deck of heroin, will send it flying if an approaching detective is spotted.

But when police are in a drug neighborhood they have no difficulty spotting addicts on the street. An experienced narcotics cop, or a longtime addict, can with surprising reliability spot a user in a group of twenty people, state with authority what kind of drug he is on, approximately how long it has been since his last fix, and whether or not he is at that moment "dirty," carrying drugs. Because heroin subdues appetite, the addict is almost always thin. He has a craving for sweets, and often carries a bottle of soda pop (although he may know that, to a detective, it is a badge of addiction). The backs of his hands are chronically puffed and swollen, from shooting in the veins there.

The addict is habitually dirty, his clothes filthy, and he stands slackly as if his body were without muscles. Waiting for a connection, he is nervous and intent, staring for minutes at a time in the direction from which he expects the pusher to come. Detectives know that when a group of addicts is standing around, talking, waiting, none of them is carrying heroin. But if you watch the group long enough, suddenly it explodes, all the addicts walking off in different directions. The pusher has appeared and soon, one by one, they will make their roundabout way to him to cop.

Once the addict has drugs on him, he keeps moving. He is about to achieve the one thing for which he lives, and he is not slow about it. His shoulders are hunched, his head is down, and he strikes out with what some detectives call a "leaving-the-set-walk," as if he had just learned where a million dollars was hidden. When the heroin addict is high, his pupils are "pinned," constricted. And though he may appear terribly sleepy, he speaks coherently. His mind wanders, he daydreams, and everything he does, he does with maddening slowness. He can take thirty minutes to tie his shoelaces. But he always resists admitting that he is on a nod. He is very sleepy, he says, and if he stops talking in midsentence, he argues that he is not nodding, only trying to phrase the sentence properly. Once the addict has had his shot and is straight, he may become admirably, though briefly, industrious, suddenly deciding to shine his shoes, brush his coat, comb his hair—all the while scolding himself bitterly for having slipped so far.

Even the seasons conspire to identify addicts. In winter, waiting to cop, they alone stand around in the snow and slush, apparently aimlessly. In summer, they alone wear long sleeves (to cover their "tracks"—collapsed veins and needle marks). Because heroin users almost always feel cold, they wear piles of sweaters, even in hot weather.

When male and female addicts gather together, in a hotel room or public bathroom, the narcotics detective knows better than to suspect sexual activity. Heroin depresses sexual desire—men may become impotent, women often do not menstruate. (If a woman gives birth while she is addicted to heroin, the infant also will be physically addicted and must live his first few days withdrawing from the drug.) For most heroin addicts a sex crime would be impossible, and they are all contemptuous of stories about the "raging, dope-fiend sex maniac."

Almost all heroin addicts are childishly immature: full of demands, empty of offerings. When they want something, they want it yesterday and they want it effortlessly. Nothing is their fault—their addiction, their degradation, their desperation. All are insecure, most dislike people, and —though the mechanics of obtaining and injecting drugs force them into relationships with other people—most would prefer to be alone.

When they are off heroin, addicts tend to be morose and restless. On heroin, when they are straight, they are pleasant, gentle, likeable. Psychiatrists who have studied them over long periods know that most of them are extremely narcissistic, that their intense preoccupation with heroin is a surface manifestation of a more profound emotional preoccupation with themselves.

In pursuit of the drug they can bring to bear extraordinary cunning, nerve, and acting ability. But once they have the fix in hand and the problem shifts from how to get drugs to how to avoid arrest, these qualities vanish. An addict who is arrested because a detective discovered heroin hidden in his pants cuff may, once he is released, immediately buy a deck of heroin and hide it in his pants cuff.

From time to time the addict may voluntarily interrupt his life on the street to enter a hospital, many of which reserve beds for addicts. His body has achieved such a high tolerance to heroin that he must shoot a huge number of bags—not just to get high, but to keep from getting sick. In the case of a prostitute, she may be getting so thin and sick-looking—so "strung out"—that she has been forced to reduce her price. In both cases the addict goes into a hospital to withdraw from the drug and get back to the point where just a bag or two will make him high.

Perhaps the dominant emotional characteristic of the addict is his enormous compulsion to abdicate all responsibility for his own life. He craves to be told what to do. If he is encouraged to go to a hospital by someone he trusts, he will go; but soon, when he finds the hospital not to his liking, he will leave, and then blame the failure not on himself but on the person who urged him to go. An addict will walk along a street openly displaying a container of drugs, all but asking to be arrested. If a detective does spot the drug and arrests him, the addict will blame it on bad luck. He thus purges himself of the responsibility of choosing between jail and abstinence, or continued addiction on the street. He feels he has left the choice to fate.

Female addict prostitutes may, for the same reason, solicit men who are almost certainly detectives. One psychiatrist reported that when one of his addict patients saw another patient in an artificial lung, she became enraged and demanded the lung for herself, unconsciously demonstrating her wish to relinquish to the lung her ultimate responsibility—breathing.

What haunts the addict are anxieties, which only heroin can relieve. In the shaky families and oppressive environment of big-city slums, anxieties pile up fast—and it is in the teeming slums that heroin is handy. From friend to friend the drug spreads inexorably among the emotionally weak and unstable.

Chapter 3

Of the hundreds of locations outside Harlem where addicts buy drugs, one of the most typical is at the corner of 71st Street where Broadway pushes through Amsterdam Avenue on its diagonal slice across Manhattan. To subway riders who use the stop there, the intersection is Sherman Square. To the drug addicts it is "Needle Park." Nothing justifies the word "park" except four or five park benches stuck together on a tiny concrete island at the center of the intersection. The nearest expanse of grass is in Central Park, two blocks east. It was here, in the neighborhood of Needle Park, that Bob and Helen lived and stole and hustled and scored and injected their drugs.

Junkies hang around Needle Park because it is surrounded by cheap hotels, needed by addict prostitutes; because three blocks away, a short walk for a sick junkie, are respectable neighborhoods good for burglary and "cracking shorts" (breaking into cars); and because, probably, a long time ago someone started selling heroin there and the area just got to be known as a good place to make a connection.

Much of the heroin in Needle Park came from a man called Little Tony—a heroin wholesaler, a business man, not himself a junkie—who lived in a very nice apartment on a pleasant East Side street. He bought heroin in "pieces" (ounces), cut it, bagged it, and handed it over on consignment to a handful of pushers—junkies themselves—who sold it for him. Pushers in New York—panic or not—do not really have to push. It's a seller's market with heroin, and junkies fight their way to any connection who has good stuff. The image of the sly pusher enticing nonusers into trying a free bag of heroin is pure myth.

The amount of payment the junkie pusher gets is the same anywhere in the city. Fifteen $3 bags are wrapped together with a rubber band (the package is called a half load). The pusher buys the package for $25, sells enough bags to recoup his investment, and uses the rest himself. Often the junkie pusher will deal "nickel bags" at $5 each, as well as $3 "treys." These come in "bundles" similar to half loads, except that the package costs $75 and consists of twenty-five $5 bags. Sometimes a junkie pusher can get half loads or bundles on consignment. But if he decides to

shoot up all the bags himself and beat the supplier for the
money, his friends will soon be remarking that they haven't
seen him around for a while. He usually keeps pushing
until he is busted or until he gets scared and decides to stop
pressing his luck with the police, and returns to less serious
crimes to finance his habit.

At the start of the panic, Bob was one of about five
junkies pushing Little Tony's stuff in Needle Park. Far
from reaching the point where he was scared enough to lay
off awhile, he was about to embark on a project far more
dangerous than mere pushing ever could be. He had decided to try to displace Little Tony as Needle Park's prime
heroin supplier. To understand why he did this you must
know something about Bob's older brother Hank.

Hank was twenty-five, with thick black hair and an intent, quiet face. He was over six feet—taller than Bob (who
was a stringy five feet eight), stronger and better-looking.
He was first arrested—for purse snatching—when he was
ten years old. He mainlined his first heroin shot when he
was fourteen, and when the panic began he had done
twenty bits in jail for a total of nine years, plus three years
in the federal narcotics hospital at Lexington, Kentucky.
"I'm the best burglar on the West Side," he boasted
proudly, and he was probably right. He had great skill and
daring—what junkies call "heart." "Burglary is my business," he explained soberly. "It's what I'm good at." In addition to heart, he had an indispensable talent for talking his
way out of tight spots.

"You see," he said, "when I go into an apartment I jam

the lock—stick some toothpicks in the keyhole and break
them off—so if the people come back I can hear them trying to get their key in and I can make it out the fire escape. But once in a while I get careless and don't jam the
lock and then—well, like once this guy come back and got
in the apartment and saw me. It was real tight, man. He
was standing there with his wife and his little kid, and I
grabbed the kid and said, 'Man, I don't want to do nothin'
to the kid, but I'm a dope fiend and I'm real sick and I got
to get out of here.' And I guess the guy thought I was
really gonna hurt the kid or something—I mean, you
couldn't blame him—and he let me go."

When it came to crime, Bob stood always in the shadow
of his brother Hank. In the junkie world, crime establishes
status. Everyone knew that Hank had once been on the
verge of being "made" by the Mafia—taken on by them
as a permanent member. He had worked for them, had
done time in jail because of jobs he did for them, and had
never ratted. He was sharp, reliable, and he had guts. Then
he went on drugs solidly and they dropped him, but his
friends knew he had almost made it, and he was still one
of the best burglars around. He had heart.

But Bob boosted cabs. He went into them when they
were parked and unlocked, and hunted around inside for
anything he could find. That was the lowest of the low.
Nothing was easier or simpler, required less nerve and produced smaller profits than boosting cabs. And when he
wasn't boosting cabs, he was living off Helen's earnings as a
prostitute, which was even worse than boosting.

Bob had tried burglary, and got caught both times. He couldn't help faltering at the crucial moment. His last attempt was so inept that it kept his friends laughing the whole six months he served on Riker's Island. He and Hank had broken the window of a candy store near Needle Park —it was about three o'clock in the morning—and Bob crawled in through the window and unlocked the door for Hank. The back of the shop was stacked with cartons of cigarettes. "Wait here," Hank whispered to Bob in the darkness, "and I'll go out and find a box to put the cigarettes in."

He left and Bob sat down behind a counter to wait. In a few minutes he heard someone tapping on the side of the window he had broken. He reached out in the dark to take the box from Hank—and grabbed the barrel of a policeman's revolver. He never mentioned an accomplice, and Hank stayed free.

When Bob came out of jail, he was determined to do something to silence the laughs of the other junkies, to demand respect and envy, and to outclass his brother. In jail, he had worked out a plan. No one ranked higher on the junkie status ladder than the supplier; not the common street pusher—anyone could do that—but the man who supplied the pushers. That took heart, cunning, business sense—and it made more money than a burglar, even Hank, could steal in a lifetime. Most junkies never tried it because it meant going through too many "changes," too many complications. A junkie's life is haunted by changes. If he goes looking for a connection and does not find him on the right corner at the right time, he grumbles about all the changes. Almost everything he is forced to do involves too many changes. He must go through changes to steal, to find a fence, to get a shot, to avoid police. He prefers simple, nonviolent crimes—theft, burglary, prostitution. He wants only to get his fix with as few problems, as few changes, as possible and be left in peace to shoot it. Supplying pushers with heroin is not for him.

But Bob's competition with his brother was putting him through more changes, he thought, than supplying ever would. After all, six months in jail for burglary was a pretty big change right there. The panic, which began just after he got out of jail, crystallized his determination to replace Little Tony as the Needle Park supplier. If he had Little Tony's job, he told himself, he wouldn't have to hustle all the time for drugs. No matter how drastically the drug supply dried up, a supplier must surely always be able to find just a little bit. You couldn't be around that much stuff— whole ounces of it—and then suddenly not be able to get even a few nickel bags. So by displacing Little Tony, Bob thought, he could insure his own supply of heroin and at the same time he could leapfrog his brother in importance and respect among the other Needle Park junkies. Instead of pushing for Little Tony, they'd be pushing for *him*. It is typical of the junkie's inability to consider the future that Bob did not for an instant seriously consider what Little Tony might have to say about a junkie moving in on him.

Bob had the characteristically childlike mind of almost all big-city street addicts: he thought only of glory and rewards, never of dangers and difficulties. The absurdity of a junkie shoving a Mafia drug supplier out of business would have been obvious—to almost anyone but Bob.

Chapter 4

Because of the addict's total preoccupation with heroin, and the twenty-four-hour-a-day concentration it takes him to stay straight, he can afford no moments idly spent with well-intentioned reformers (unless, as is quite often the case, he senses an opportunity to con the well-wisher out of a few dollars). But just after his release from jail, when drugs were beginning to get scarce and addicts started to talk of panic, Bob ran into a square he didn't want to shake loose too fast. The man was myself, a magazine writer trying to learn as much as possible about drug addicts. For a week I had spent up to twenty hours a day in neighborhoods popular with junkies, looking for an addict

who wouldn't mind having a square around. All I wanted, I
told Bob, was to stay with him for a few weeks to see the
way he lived. I explained that I did not want to change him,
to reform him, or have him arrested. I only wanted to see
what his life was like. He nodded solemnly as I spoke, but—
I realized later—he easily recognized the customary possi-
bilities. No square could resist a junkie's tale of woe and
sickness: a runny nose, watering eyes, a few moans from
stomach cramps, stories about not eating or sleeping for
four days, and any square was worth at least three bucks,
enough for a bag of heroin. If this guy really wanted to
hang around for a few weeks, Bobby was thinking, he
could be a real good mark. Helen was the best con artist
around, and pretty too. The guy might even be a trick.
Wait till Helen got her hooks into him. She'd milk the guy
dry in four days, a week for sure. And what difference did
it make, anyway? The guy wasn't a cop, that's for sure.
Why would a narco waste time following around after a
junkie. If he was smart he could bust a dozen junkies in one
day just by keeping his eyes open around Needle Park.
Having a writer around wouldn't hurt anyone, and he
might just turn out to be a real gold mine. He wasn't a
priest or a do-gooder or anything like that. Just so long as
he didn't want to bust anyone, or preach or get between
anyone and their fix, what could it matter?

"Sure," Bob told me, "hang around all you like. You're a
nice guy. You look straight, you know what I mean? I
mean, a lot of people I see them and right away I don't
think too much of them. They're not right, you know

what I mean? Somethin' tells you they're phonies. But you're not like that. You ought to meet Helen, this girl I go with. You'd like her, I think. I mean she's not like other junkies. If you saw her on the street when she wasn't too sick you probably'd most likely as not wouldn't even know she was a junkie. She's not like these other scanks around here. She's real nice. You might like her. And she'd like you too."

We had been talking in a cafeteria on West 72nd Street, just off Amsterdam Avenue, about a block from Needle Park. We were on the second floor, at a table near the window where Bob could keep an eye on the street. You never knew when a good connection might walk by, or a trick Helen had been looking for, or someone you knew you could con out of a buck or two. The other tables around us were crowded, and the place echoed with the clamor of plates and trays and silverware.

The conversation stopped and we just sat there, drinking our coffee. Bob wiped his nose.

"How do you feel?" I asked.

"How do I always feel?" Bob smiled faintly so I would know the remark wasn't meant to sound smart. "I haven't had anything since yesterday morning. Man, it's real tight out there. You know, they've started selling nickel bags for $7. Man, it ain't been that bad in a *long* time. We got a panic, that's what it looks like." He wiped his nose again and squirmed in his seat. Then he looked out the window down to the sidewalk. "Man, if I don't get somethin' soon, I don't know what I might do, what I might *have* to do. It scares me, you know, thinkin' about what I could do to get stuff." I put my hand in my pocket, trying to be casual, but Bob knew what was going on in that pocket. "I scare myself. I think if I went out there with a knife or somethin' and I hurt someone who hadn't done nothin' to nobody . . . I ain't never done nothin' like that. I mean not to a square person. I've taken off connections and people like that, but not a square. Man, I hope I *never* do nothin' like that."

I took my hand out of my pocket and slipped Bob five dollars, half of what I had at first thought of giving him.

"Thanks," he said. "Thanks a lot." We made a date to meet in the same place at ten o'clock the next morning. Bob said he would bring Helen so I could meet her, and if she said it was all right for me to hang around with them it would be all right for sure.

Chapter 5

The next morning at ten I sat down at the same table over-looking the street and waited. In ten minutes I spotted Bob coming up 72nd Street, walking fast, weaving quickly around and past the slower pedestrians ahead of him. He was alone. I watched him disappear into the revolving door just under the window and then almost immediately heard a crash of trays and plates downstairs. Someone yelled in Spanish and Bob yelled back, angrily, almost drunkenly, cursing a Puerto Rican cleanup boy whose trays he had toppled. Bob came charging up the stairs, saw me, walked quickly to the table—almost knocking over empty chairs on the way—and sat down.

"What happened downstairs?" I asked.

"Nothing, some spic jerk." He seemed to relax a little as he settled at the table, then suddenly he stood up and looking back at the stairs asked for a dime. I gave him some change and he went back downstairs. Ten minutes later he was back with two cups of coffee and two sweet rolls. Bob took a long noisy drink of the hot coffee. His face and arms were streaked with dirt and his shirt looked as if it had been worn and slept in for a month.

"Man," Bob started, out of nowhere, "do you know how *degrading* it is to wake up in a bathroom?" He shook his head solemnly and took another slurping drink of coffee, emptying the cup. I pushed the other cup over to him. He wasn't drunk, but he certainly wasn't sober either. He was high on barbiturates, goofballs, GB's. Barbiturates are sleeping pills, but taken excessively they may produce not sleepiness but a frighteningly unpredictable aggressiveness, such as Bob was displaying now. He was, in the junkies' word, "goofing."

"Where's Helen?" I asked.

"Oh, man," Bob answered, seriously, as if the words gave him physical pain, "I don't know. I wish I knew. She could'a been busted, or in a hospital, or somethin' worse or anything. I ain't seen her in two days now. I waited for her all night in the park. I should'a been out workin', boostin' cabs, 'cause I ain't had nothin' since that five you gave me yesterday. And you know something? I got beat for half of that—or rather I had to give away half of it, which was just like gettin' beat 'cause I didn't really know the guy." He

spread the fingers of his left hand and while he spoke
touched them one by one as if to give a logical progression
to his unordered thoughts.

"I bought a trey with four of what you gave me. And
lucky I didn't have to use all five, this panic is so bad—and
I picked up another dollar some place for this transitor radio
that doesn't even work that I got out of a cab, and that
made two more dollars that I had for some GB's. *Only*"—
he touched another finger, proceeding to a new point—
"*only*, I couldn't score, see, 'cause of the panic. I couldn't
find *nobody*. Not Shorty, or Sonny, or Buster—and, man,
Buster has got the *good* stuff, I mean even in this panic he's
always got good stuff. I don't know how he does it. No one
was anywhere, and I mean I really looked.

"So anyway, this Spanish kid tells me he can cop up on
112th Street. So I never saw him before, I mean just around
a little bit, but I never really talked to him or nothin' and
I didn't want to put my money in his hand and then get
beat for it, not when it was all I had and I didn't know
when I'd see Helen again or be able to get any more. But I
was desperate and I figured I couldn't get nothin' myself so
I had to take the chance, so I says okay and I give him the
six dollars—yours and the one I put with it. He goes uptown. And I wait and I wait and I wait and I wait. I wait
till about three—in the mornin'—till I'm like *sure* I got beat.
I would'a been mad, but I was too sick. 'Cause like I don't
go for anyone beatin' me, especially when I'm sick. That
ain't no good, to beat a guy when he's sick. So I go up to
112th Street and I figure I'll look for him. Now, that's dan-

gerous up there 'cause there's no whites up there at all and you don't know who might try to take you off, even if you ain't got nothin', 'cause they don't know that till after they try to get it from you. So anyway I go up there and I look for him and I just happen to see him, just happen by luck to see him, and he sees me see him and for some strange reason he don't run—'cause he could'a if he'd wanted to and I never could'a caught him, not up there and feelin' as sick as I was. But he comes over and says he had all kinds of trouble scoring and was just on his way back downtown. So he had the stuff and so we got off. I had to give him half, so all I had was half a trey."

He smiled, a sheepish, little-boy smile. "And then a little while ago I had some GB's, to hold me till I can do somethin' to get more stuff. I felt *so* awful. I woke up in the fourth-floor bathroom of the Martell Hotel and said to myself, 'I gotta hurry, I gotta hurry, 'cause I said I'd meet him at ten and it's *gotta* be later than that.' So I just took these GB's and came over."

He took a bite out of a roll and drank more of the coffee. Then quietly, the rapid-fire fury of his speech completely dissipated, he looked up from the coffee and asked simply, "You got the time?"

"Eleven."

"That's all? I should feel worse than I do. Those GB's did good for me. I don't use them often, that's why." He paused for several seconds, thinking. "I wish I knew where Helen was. It ain't like her to stay away this long. Two nights ago she went with this trick and ordinarily she'd come around the next afternoon—at the latest—and she'd have money, or maybe even she'd have already scored and we'd get high right then."

He was staring out of the window down onto the street and suddenly shouted, "Hey, there's Sammy! He owes me two bucks." He banged on the window with a spoon. People at the other tables thought he was drunk. Sammy looked up at the window, waved, and came in and sat with us.

He was younger than Bob—about nineteen—just as short but thirty or forty pounds heavier, almost fat. He was only "chipping," using drugs occasionally when they were handy, and had not yet acquired a habit. His face was white and round with bright sparkling eyes and a quick spoken wit to match them.

"Boy, you're stoned," he said to Bobby. His eyes were on me, an open, friendly look, though he had never met me.

"This is a friend of mine, a writer," Bob said. "Want a roll?" He offered Sammy the remaining roll, but Sammy shook his head.

"I just saw Helen," he said. "She was looking for you."
Bob was stunned. "Where?"
"In the park. She was with Farrell going to the Martell."
"Was she straight?"
"She didn't look sick. Anyway, she's probably getting off up there now."

Bob slammed his fist on the table, rattling the cups, and got up and headed for the stairs. Sammy and I chased after him over to 72nd and Broadway, then across Broadway to the Martell and up to Farrell's room. Helen opened the door and we walked in.

"Bobby, I'm so glad you're all right," she said, throwing her arms around him. "I've been looking all over for you. I've had everyone looking. Where've you been?" She released him, but didn't let him answer.

"You look sick, buddy," she said, "Here, I've got something for you." She walked over to a small table, picked up a white packet about the size of a commemorative postage stamp, tore it open slowly, carefully, and emptied the contents, a white powder, into a bottle top.

She was exceptionally pretty for a junkie, and would no doubt have been a lot prettier if she weren't so strung out. She could have used a couple of months in a hospital. She was about five feet seven inches but looked as if she didn't weigh more than a hundred pounds. She was wearing blue slacks and a white blouse covered with a white v-neck sweater which itself was covered with a black cardigan. Dark red hair fell down to her shoulders, framing a thin face with large blue eyes.

"Come over here, Bobby," she called. "I can't shoot the stuff across the room."

"Helen," Bob said, staying at the door, "don't give me that sweet-talk stuff. Where the hell have you been?" His eyes were glued to the white powder and had followed it from the packet to the bottle top like a dog watching its food being prepared.

"Look, Bobby, you want this or not? I'm not so straight

I couldn't use it myself, you know, and maybe Sammy here could use a little too. So are you gonna stand there yelling all day or do you want it?"

Bobby took an eyedropper off the table, held a match under the cooker, and gave himself the shot. Then he sat down, silent, and started to comb his hair.

Helen looked at Sammy and me. "I gotta do everything for that nut," she said affectionately. "I gotta turn tricks for the bread, then score, then find him, and then practically put the needle in his arm for him. And he wants to yell at me." She looked at Bobby in the chair. He was high now, smiling his little-boy smile, a child lovingly reprimanded by its mother.

"Now," she said warmly to me, "you're not The Man, I hope?" knowing that I wasn't or I wouldn't be there with Bob and Sammy.

"He's a friend of Bobby's," Sammy said. "Where's Farrell?"

"I dunno," she said, "Out there some place." She waved a hand at the window looking out on Needle Park. Farrell was a square, an electrician, and he worked nights for the Transit Authority, repairing subway power lines. He used a kind of strong nylon clothesline to tie cables together, and short arm's-length pieces of it lay here and there around the room. Junkies who conned him into letting them use his room to get off in found it just the thing for tourniquets.

"Poor Farrell," Helen said, turning on the charm for me —a new square, a new mark. "I don't know why he puts up with us. He goes to work all night and then comes back

here and lets us con him out of his dough and use his room
to shoot up in. Do you know how many hotels he's been
kicked out of 'cause of us? Must be over five. A really
swell, nice guy." She laughed, and turned toward Bobby,
who was nodding in the chair.

"Hey, Bobby, remind me to be nicer to Farrell, will you?
The poor jerk." Bobby kept sitting there, nodding, and
didn't answer. She looked back at me, the smile gone. "He
never did like Farrell, or any of my tricks, for that matter. I
think he thinks I'm sweet on him or something. Sweet on
him. Can you imagine that? Me sweet on that fat, bald old
creep?"

"Helen," Bobby was trying to hold his head up, but the
eyelids were drooping. "Helen, I got to talk to you. I got
to talk to you about something—something very important,
Helen, *very* important."

Helen went over and sat on his lap. "Yeah, honey, what is
it, honey, tell me about it, what is it?"

Bobby spread his fingers again. "Well," he said, "I got
this idea on the rock about somethin' I'm gonna do, somethin' very, very, very big that I'm gonna do."

"Yeah, honey, well what is it? What is it?" She snuggled
her face in his neck and he started whispering in her ear.
After a minute she jumped up. "Bobby, you got to be out
of your head, right all the way out of your head. Little
Tony'd murder you, *murder* you. You're crazy, buddy!
Crazy!"

She stopped shouting and lit a cigarette.

"Helen," Bobby yelled from the chair, "if anyone murders me it'll be because you're shooting off your big mouth. You want to tell the whole world or something? And then I'll go out there and get my head knocked off. And you'd like that."

"All right, all right. We'll talk about it later. Let's get out of here. I been in this crummy room all day. Let's get outa here."

All of us—Bobby, Helen, Sammy, and myself—left the room and walked down the dim, dusty, shoe-worn wooden stairs to the street. We crossed Broadway to the benches on the concrete island in the middle of the intersection.

It was hot and sunny and the benches were filled with junkies sitting shoulder to shoulder—some sniffling in withdrawal, staring anxiously up and down Broadway, searching desperately for approaching connections; others on the nod from recent shots, their heads bobbing forward and sideways onto the shoulders of their neighbors.

"Shove it over there, man, you can't have the whole damn park, you know," Helen said to three young girls on one of the benches. Two of them laughed a greeting at her and pushed over, lifting along with them the third girl, who was almost completely unconscious from goofballs. We all squeezed onto the bench. Helen introduced me around, and no one seemed to care the least bit that I was there.

"Man," one of the girls started, "you hang around here for very long and you'll see everything. I don't know what it is you want to see, but man you'll see it what*ever* it is." Buses, trucks, and cabs roared past on Broadway in front of us and Amsterdam Avenue behind. At times pedestrians who had been marooned on the island between lights formed into clots near the junkies, but seemed not to notice them.

"You know," the young girl went on, "if you tossed a net over this place"—she waved an arm to include the entire intersection and the surrounding sidewalks and hotels and corner luncheonettes—"at about 4 a.m. all you'd catch would be junkies, Johns, queers, and cops. Unless maybe you just *happened* to get a taxi with some squares just passing through."

"Hey, there's Irene!" Helen shouted, and rushed through traffic across the street to bring back a short, pretty girl about twenty-one. We squeezed over even more to make room for her. "She just got out of the house," Helen said, meaning the Women's House of Detention in Greenwich Village.

"But baby, what's this?" Helen laughed, running her hand over the back of Irene's black hair, cut short in the manner of a Lesbian.

"Well, you know how it is in the house, honey," Irene said. "Things go better this way. If you can't beat 'em, join 'em." She told the group how she had been busted. They listened earnestly, leaning toward her to catch the words over the noise of the traffic.

"I walk up to this John out here, see, and I stick my finger in his back"—she held up a very nonviolent-looking finger—"and I lowers my voice way down deep and threatening, you know?, and I says, like this, 'Put up your hands and give me your money.' If he'd turned around, I guess

I'd just have curled up my pretty little finger and passed out cold. Anyway, I get his money but then when I'm running away The Man spots me—you know Burdick, the narco, the tall guy with glasses?—well anyway, they busted me for robbery. 'Robbery!' I said to them. 'With my finger? Man, you've got to be out of your skull. I'm not a *robber*, I'm a *prostitute*.' But anyhow they got me. So how's things been?"

Across the street a slight wispy Lesbian named Penny was shouting at some friends through the window of a luncheonette. She was a goofball addict and Helen explained that her wild behavior while she was high, which was most of the time, had created such havoc in the local coffee shops that they no longer let her in. Today she stood outside on the sidewalk, yelling and waving at the friends inside, and then, suddenly, laughed uproariously and went running down the street with another girl.

Joey was there too—sitting on the bench, walking around, talking to the other junkies as they came and went in their various searches for connections, fences, Johns, someone to con. He had just finished three years in Leavenworth for smuggling heroin from Mexico and now he had had enough and wanted desperately to stay off drugs and be square. He was trying to get a job. "But how can you explain three years out of your life? And no one in his right mind is going to hire a junkie."

A boy named Mike sat down for a few minutes. He was on amphetamines, stimulants, and had been shooting *bombitas*, small glass ampules of a drug called Desoxyn. In Harlem they cost a dollar, in Needle Park the price is $1.50 or $2. Mike had the customary symptoms of an amphetamine user. He talked constantly, could not sit still, and his arms and face were covered with sores where he had picked at the skin, sometimes with the illusion that bugs were crawling underneath. He was a Murphy Man, which meant that he supported himself by posing as a pimp. He told Johns he found around the park that he could get them girls, but they'd have to come up with a little money "in front," before they saw the goods. He'd take the money and hand over a key with a number on it, instructing his quarry to go to that number room at a certain hotel and wait for the girl. When the John got to the room and tried the key, he'd discover he'd been duped. Mike found the Murphy game— for which when caught he usually did thirty days—considerably less harrowing than his old profession as a Badger Man. In that scheme he had worked with a prostitute, waiting for her to get a John into her room, then barging in and announcing angrily that he was the girl's husband and was going to take the John apart limb by limb. Then he allowed his fury to be stilled by cash. That kind of action could get you a lot of money—everything the John had on him— but it could also get you a few years for assault.

Across the street, near where Penny had been yelling through the window, stood Nick, a tall, trench-coated Negro. Nick was a takeoff artist, and a good man to ignore. He supported his habit by taking off (robbing) connections, and almost anyone else in the junkie world who appeared to have money.

Sonny Puck was around, too. Sonny was always around. He was in his late thirties, old for an addict, wore a red goatee and spoke in a rasping, throaty, endless monotone that became very irritating very quickly. He thought of himself as a kind of intellectual, an authority on all kinds of drugs, and had done time for counterfeiting, a rather classy crime for an addict. At the moment, like Sammy, he had only a chippy, and got most of the heroin he needed by hanging around other addicts who occasionally turned him on with a taste, gave him a weak shot from their own supply. But Sonny's habit was growing worse and he was turning to burglary to support it. Even as a burglar, he affected style.

"The beard helps," he explained. "You know, it gives me class. Like a doorman or someone like that don't expect a burglar to have a beard. So I put on a fairly decent suit, you know, and I carry an attaché case, and I just breeze right into some high-class apartment house in Sutton Place or Tudor City and if the doorman looks at me I says to him real sharp and authoritative, 'Internal Revenue,' and keep right on going. They never stop me."

As it always is, the talk that day was of drugs. Which is better, someone asked, heroin mixed with a *bombita* or with cocaine? Cocaine and *bombitas* are both stimulants, and combined with heroin, a depressant, they produce an electrifying "rush" or "flash" far more pleasurable to the addict than heroin alone. The mixture is called a "speedball." Everyone on the benches pointed out that while cocaine is better than a *bombita*, it is also much more expensive. So for the money, a *bombita* and heroin cannot be topped. Some-one said they knew someone who liked to shoot glue. No one else had heard of that. Sniffing glue, yes, but not shoot-ing it. They had heard of people doing something to para-goric and shoe polish and then shooting it, but the high was reported to be no good. Heroin, of course, was the best. Heroin and a *bombita*. It gave the best high, completely relaxed, not a problem in the world. But that's not really the best high, one addict said. Do you know what the best high *really* is? The voice was serious and everyone turned and stayed very quiet to hear, maybe, of a new kind of high that was better than heroin, better than anything else. The best high—the voice was low and somber, heads leaned close to listen—was death. Silence. Man, that's outa sight, that's somethin' else. Yeah, no feelin' at all. Everyone agreed. The best high of all was death.

Chapter 6

We were sitting in the sun on the benches that day talking of drugs when a skinny junkie came charging across Amsterdam Avenue and stopped breathless in front of Helen.

"Helen, you got to come over here, kid, you got to come fast. Frankie's OD'ing up in Marcie's room in the Reynolds. He needs help bad, honey. You gotta come right now." Helen was smarter than most of the other junkies, and one area in which her brilliance was widely recognized was in the treatment of an OD, an overdose—a shot that unexpectedly contains more heroin than the body can survive. Helen always knew what to do about an overdose. She got up and, followed by me and a couple of other junkies who

were straight enough to care about a little excitement, ran
with the skinny junkie back to the Reynolds Hotel. We
went in through the bar, which joined the hotel lobby near
some stairs around the corner from the desk, making it possible to get upstairs unobserved by the clerks. We ran up to
the fourth floor and Helen knocked on a door. A girl
opened the door to the length of the chain lock, recognized
the junkies, closed the door again to remove the chain, and
let us in. Frankie was sitting in a chair, his body doubled
forward between his legs so that his head almost touched
the linoleum floor. A small baby lay naked on the bed.

"Okay, all you guys get outa here," Helen ordered to
everyone except Bobby, me, and the girl who had let us in.
When the others had left, she grabbed Frankie under the
shoulders and tried to lift him out of the chair. "Bobby,
give me a hand here, will you? Marcie, go soak some towels
in cold water." Marcie disappeared into the bathroom and
Helen and Bobby got Frankie on his feet.

Helen put her lips to Frankie's ear and shouted. "Open
your eyes, Frankie! Try to wake up! You took too much
stuff, Frankie! You got to wake up! You got to fight it,
Frankie! You got to fight it!"

Marcie came back with a wet towel. "What did he
have?" Helen asked, trying to wrap the towel around his
head without letting him fall down.

"I told him not to. I said he shouldn't—that it was too
much," Marcie said.

"Never mind that, what did he have?"

"He took five Doridens and a shot of junk. But it was
Sandy's stuff, real dynamite."

"Okay, Frankie, let's walk," Helen shouted. "Come on, Frankie. You got to help us. You got to walk. Don't go to sleep, Frankie. Come on. Walk! Walk!"

Frankie mumbled something. Helen and Bobby dumped him back into the chair and Helen started to slap his face with the towel. Bobby sat on the bed next to the baby. He had never met Marcie before. "Your kid?" he asked.

"Yeah." Marcie was Puerto Rican, about seventeen years old.

"Ain't it got no clothes?"

"It had some, but this lady that was taking care of it for me said she was gonna turn it in to the cops or someone 'cause she said I shouldn't have it, so I took it away and I left the clothes." She turned to Helen, who was still slapping Frankie with the towel.

"Helen, how long is he gonna *be* like that? I mean I got a trick comin' up here in about twenty minutes and I can't miss it 'cause he sees me regular and he gives me forty, you know, and I can't miss it, 'cause like I really need the bread."

"Look, honey," Helen said, "if he dies then we can just dump the body on the bed next to the kid and you can all turn the trick together and that'll be wild, won't it, so don't bug me, baby. I'm doing the best I can."

"Well I sure don't want him to *die*, but I got this trick like I told you comin' up here in maybe twenty minutes and he's not gonna want *him* in here." She pointed a thin brown arm at Frankie, slumped in the chair.

Frankie began to moan. "Get him up again," Helen said, and Bobby helped her hoist him to his feet. They walked him in circles around the room. He began to come to, mumbled for a few minutes—trying to keep his legs under him—and then put together his first complete sentence: "Man, *that* was a *good* bag."

"You were lucky it wasn't better, buddy," Helen said, settling him back into the chair. She knew as well as any medical examiner that almost every day in New York City a junkie dies of an overdose, some sold intentionally by pushers who think the addict has been "stooling" to detectives. Sometimes, she knew, these "hotshots" contain no heroin at all, but rat poison. Addicts call this type of hotshot a "ten-cent pistol" because the poison costs a dime but is as effective as a gun. Helen had treated many OD's and had seen quite a few bodies disposed of—tossed out windows, hauled into alleys. Once she had heard a strange sound outside her hotel room ("It was like shhhhh, shhhhh"), and when she looked she saw two junkies dragging a body down the hall.

"Can you walk, Frankie?" Helen yelled into his ear. No answer.

"Frankie, can you walk?" He mumbled something.

Someone knocked on the door.

Marcie was frantic. "What can I do now? What can I do?" She lunged for the bed and scooped up the baby, not really knowing what she was going to do with it.

"In the sink!" Helen ordered, grabbing Frankie's arm. "Marcie, put the baby in the sink. Bobby, help me get Frankie into the bathroom."

Helen and Bobby lugged Frankie into the bathroom, sat

him on the toilet, and tried to hold him more or less up-right. Marcie put the baby in the sink. The knocking came again.

"Not like that, stupid," Helen said. "You want him to bust his skull?" She took off a sweater and used it to cushion the baby's head against the side of the sink. I crowded into the bathroom with them. "Please be quiet," Marcie pleaded, closing the door. "He'll run if he hears anyone in here, and I got to have this bread."

"Okay, okay," Helen said impatiently. "Close the door and let him in. First rule of hustling, honey. Never keep a trick waiting in the hall. And Marcie . . ."

"Yeah?"

"Enjoy yourself." Helen laughed and shut the bathroom door. Frankie was sitting stupefied on the toilet, supported by Bobby. The baby lay placidly in the sink. Helen sat down on the edge of the bathtub and lit a cigarette. She looked at me. "Some life, huh? Never a dull minute. A guy on his way back from an OD, a naked kid in a sink, and some dumb spic broad hustling a guy who's probably too stupid to know she's on junk. Some world."

In fifteen minutes Marcie opened the bathroom door and then walked back to the mirror in the bedroom and fixed her hair. The baby began to cry.

"Hey, Marcie," Helen said, "I don't want to sound like a social worker or anything but the kid's not gonna like that sink forever. Maybe you should even feed it, now that you've got a little cash."

"Yeah," Marcie said indifferently, still combing her hair,

"I'll take care of that in a minute. Thanks a lot. Can you get him out of here?" She nodded disapprovingly at Frankie.

Bobby and Helen left, supporting Frankie between them. We all went back to the benches and sat down. Frankie was nodding, but conscious enough to be out of danger.

"Now," Helen said to Bobby, as if nothing had happened, "what's this stuff about you putting Little Tony out of business?"

They sat there together on the bench whispering, rubbing against the other junkies on either side of them but completely withdrawn now to themselves, on their own little island in the middle of Needle Park.

"Well, like I was trying to say when you started screaming at me before," Bobby started, "I got this idea on the rock. Like why should I push Little Tony's stuff? Tony's got five guys out here dealing for him and why should they? I mean why should I? Hank goes out and hits some place and he's got a lot of loot and he's turnin' everyone on and he's some kind of hero or something and all I ever get is busted and serve time. I don't have to do that, Helen, I don't *have* to live like that. 'Cause you may not realize it, like all the time we've been together you may not have thought so, but I can be a pretty sharp guy when I want to, too, you know. And so I figure I'll get my own stuff and deal it and it'll be better stuff than Tony's 'cause Tony never had anything but garbage, you know that, and I'll put him right out of business. And then if this really does turn out to be a real bad panic, well then too I'll—we'll—

always have stuff 'cause you know a really good dealer with good connections can always like find a little stuff here or there. I mean like he's not gonna be kickin' in the streets, not if he knows his way around. And you know I can get pieces from Santo, Helen. Like before, just after I first started dealin' for Tony, Santo said he could get me a piece any time I wanted, 'cause he's not married to Tony you know. He has a little action on the side, too, that even Tony don't know about, and when he's not cutting Tony's stuff for him he's dealing pieces himself. So you know I can get a piece every now and then from him, and before you know it I'll have five guys dealing for me—for *me*—right here in Needle Park."

All this time, as Bobby spoke, Helen sat with her arms folded over her sweater, her head tilted toward Bobby's lips, listening very intently, thinking very hard. "So try it," she said finally when he was through. "I mean you're right, what have you got to lose, right?"

"That's right," Bobby said. "What have I got to lose?"

Chapter 7

That night Helen went to work, looking for a John, and I took Bobby to a room I had rented in the Martell Hotel. We stood at the window and looked down on the flashing neon lights of Broadway. We watched Helen talking to a John in front of a drugstore a block away on 72nd Street. Helen and the John walked around the corner together and Bobby said, "They're going to the Talbot. He must have lots of loot 'cause that's a better hotel than these other places. Maybe he'll let her keep the room a while. I hope so 'cause she's really tired, you know, and she could use some sleep. I really wish I could do more for her. 'Cause like she really depends on me."

He sat down in a chair and started talking. He had shot up a *bombita* just before going to the room, and now he was all words. Speech flowed straight from his brain in a steady rush. Just as a paralytic's every step is twisted by his affliction, so every word Bobby spoke was colored by the symptoms of his disease—self-deception, immaturity, insecurity, guilt.

"Like I always should'a done more for her. And not just for her. For everybody. For my mother and my father and my brothers and like for everybody. But it seems like I been using stuff for so long, that's all there is, you know what I mean? Like that's all there is. Like ever since I was thirteen. I smoked some pot then. No, I think it was the year before. I think it was closer between eleven and twelve. Then I used some junk about thirteen. And I've seen drugs practically all my life. My brother was already hooked, not just starting but already hooked, at thirteen when he was going to school. And then he went into the hospital with hepatitis, and my other brother started when he was about thirteen or fourteen. And when I started, it was like with these other guys that I was hanging around with, like we had more or less like a gang. And we used to have gang wars with the Spanish guys, the Comanche Dragons. As close as I can remember, this guy, Joe, started bringing sticks of pot around and selling them for a dollar. Like he'd been doing it for quite a while. And I was going with this girl, Ann, at the time. I went with her two years. And like I used to walk the straight and narrow line. I got a job, and kept good hours. And then I think I had an argument with her or something like that, and instead of going drinking to get drunk, I went and bought a stick of pot. And I choked my brains out. I was started.

"Eventually I started taking Benzedrine and goofballs, yellow jackets. And from there, like that's the first time I ever held drugs—heroin—in my hand. I gave this kid, Eddie, $5 to go uptown and get us some pot. And I went up with him, but he told me to wait a couple of blocks away. And when I went up there, he told me he could get a couple of bags of junk, heroin. I told him to get two for me and it didn't mean anything to me 'cause I hadn't used it. About fifteen or twenty minutes later, he comes running up to me, and he tells me the guy who was selling to him got busted. So I figured this guy's beating me for my $5, so I didn't believe him. So we started walking down the block to a pizza place to wait. He said, 'Let's wait and see what happens.' As we're walking, this car stops maybe three or four cars ahead of us, 'cause it's going too fast to stop by us. So they're narcos and this is the first time I ever got searched by a narcotics cop. They searched us and everything and they asked my friend if he was waiting for some Spanish guy whose name was Chico. Was he waiting for him and was he buying any pot from him? And we told him no. So then I knew that the kid was telling the truth, that this guy Chico did get busted.

"The cops told us to get out of the neighborhood. So we walked maybe two blocks and we finally got to the pizza place, and we waited and he told me he had tossed the stuff under a car before he was searched, and we went back and

found it. And that was Christmas Eve. That was the first
time I ever got high on a skin pop. And ever since then,
boy, I've been going real strong. My first run was about
three and a half years, between thirty-six and forty months
before I got busted and had to kick in jail. And I'll tell you,
to find somebody *now* on the streets *today* that you can
really call has a habit like I had then would really be doing
something. I mean it's not like it used to be. I've seen guys
come in jail, and like the expression, 'they kicked the habit
on the elevator.' They come from the bullpen to The
Tombs up to their floor. They came in and in two or three
days they're eating, sleeping, doing pushups. I've never been
that lucky. A lot of the junk today I could either put in my
coffee or on a cake 'cause it's mostly sugar and quinine.
The stuff is very weak. It's not like it used to be. Like when
I first started, the purest you could get was 97.6 or something close to that, and a piece of that stuff, if you could
get that, by the time it went through all the channels, being cut all them times, you could still cut it maybe seven to
one or eight to one, like make eight pieces out of one piece.
And then at that time, for a piece, you'd pay maybe $200.
Now today, if you buy your piece, you'd be very lucky if
you could get a three-to-one cut, make three pieces out of
one for $500 or $600. It's that weak. Today if you were
buying an ounce and cutting it and bagging it, a $5 bag
would actually cost you, I mean me, maybe $2. So there's a
$3 profit on each bag you sell. So if you get a hundred bags,
that's $300 profit, plus you still have your money to recop
with. And I could sell in a day maybe close to two hundred

bags, maybe more, sometimes less. On a good night I could sell maybe a piece, a piece and a half. Like, when I first started dealing for Tony, as hard as it was in the neighborhood and as many times as I was getting stopped by the narcos, I was afraid to hide it any place, 'cause like a lot of times a junkie will come up to you and say, 'Give me three bags.' And you tell him, 'Okay, wait here.' And you go to where you have it hidden. Meanwhile he's got somebody else watching you and he's trying to find out where you stash it. And the next time you go back it's gone. You just don't find it no more. So I was afraid of that happening. Of course, it actually wasn't mine. I was just making a commission on it from Tony. And like this panic we're getting now, $3 bags I could sell for $4, and $5 bags for $6.

"First I used to carry twenty, thirty, sixty bags. The most was 125 bags. Now, I was coming down the stairs one night and I had everything on me, and I had just finished getting off, and I hit the second floor, and something told me, 'Bobby, hide it,' and I just walked into the door and stuck it in the fire hose. And I no sooner turned around to go back out the door . . . it took me from the time to open the door, hide it, and get back to the door—tops—fifteen seconds . . . and when I opened the door, I actually bumped into this detective, and there was another one behind him. Now I was just plain lucky then. If they had had me, they would have had me up tight. I would have had some felonies on me. And after that I wouldn't carry it unless I was taking it from the East Side over to the West, and that would be in a cab. And like now I stand on the corner, or sit on the benches or in a restaurant, and somebody will come up to me and say, 'Bobby, give me three bags.' I go up and get it, come down the stairs, and I have them walk up the corner a bit, or I might have it stashed up the block. I walk them up the block and give it to them. But I'd always be where I could watch the stash to see that nobody goes near it. And I'd walk him kind of out of sight so no one could see it.

"But like up to now I've only pushed to keep my habit up. And I'll tell you, when people tell you like they're using $50 a day, they can't tell you that. They don't know what they're using. There's no set price on a habit as far as I'm concerned. Like I might find old Joe Schmo today and buy three bags from him and find that one bag straightens me out. Now, okay, so I'll time my shot and get away with $15 today. Tomorrow I can't find Joe Schmo so I go find Larry the Jerk, and I buy three off him and one don't straighten me out and two don't straighten me out, and sometimes three won't straighten me out. So actually what you use depends on the quality of the stuff. You can't say like you used this much and that much. I used to use a lot. Even today, if I have ten bags in the morning, I won't have anything left that night, or maybe not even that afternoon. I just can't hold on to stuff without shooting it. I won't actually get greedy, and shoot it all at once, but like whenever it enters my mind to get off, I just get off. I can't hold on to it. That's why Helen hides it from me and tells me she doesn't have it. Then in the morning she'll give me my wake-up. Otherwise I'll shoot my wake-up and be sick in the morning. Like recently I kind of got out of the habit because things are getting up tight with this panic out there. It's hard to get stuff. Then, if you can find the stuff, you need twice as much money. Then if you have to put the money in someone else's hand, you have to worry about them coming back. It's the chances you got to take. And then I just stopped taking the chances. I'd go sick for hours and hours. Otherwise I'd have to go out sick and steal again. So I just wouldn't put the money in anybody's hand unless I knew they actually had something.

"When I first started on junk and started stealing, I think I made more money out of taxi cabs than the owners of the companies did. I used to hit taxi cabs every day, three and four of them every day, take the changers out of them. Nine out of ten times, I got a portable radio. I always had portable radios. Small changers would hold about maybe $12 and big ones would hold maybe $22, $23. Or else I'd hit a cigar box full of change. But last year, during winter, I was out working, hitting cabs, and it was almost time for the meet with the connection. We used to have two meets a day and this is the second and if I miss it I can't see her until the next day, and she had the best stuff around and I was hooked on her stuff. So anything else wouldn't have done too much for me. And I just happened to see this cab and it wasn't the kind of window that I could just snap and have the silver thing on the fly window snap off. I kind of had to put the screwdriver up in the glass and shatter the whole glass. And I went into the cab looking for the changer, expecting maybe to find at the tops $20, and I come up with $500 in bills. And I had a ball, had a party. That's the time when I was trying to get into Manhattan General Hospital. I went in the day after getting the $500 and came out the next.

"And when I came out three big guys jumped me down on 18th Street and Second Avenue. This time I had to stab a colored guy, 'cause he got the money from me. They couldn't get the money at first 'cause I kept fighting them off. They had me on the ground, kicked me, pushed me, and I had the money in my hand but my hand was in my pocket, and I had gray silk pants on from this suit I had, and the whole leg came right off but the pocket was still in my hand and they couldn't get it. So like they let up a little and as I was getting up I took my hand out of my pocket to push myself up with my hands, and the nigger got his hand in my pocket and pulled it out.

"Now meantime I took my knife out. So he was going to run and I stuck him in the stomach with it, and he doubled over and I gave him a small cut on his face. Now, I thought that he had all the money 'cause I didn't see any money passed or anything like that. So the two Spanish guys, they got in the wind and they started running. So I figured I had the money here with me and so I threw him up against the wall, and everything, and I got $80. I got the money that he had on him. So somehow without me seeing it he must have passed it, or else he was just slicker than I was and he hid it on him and I couldn't find it. So I lost all that money 'cause I went in the hospital.

"And I was doing it more for Helen than me. She asked me to go in. And when I got in, the medication helped me, and I wasn't sick or anything like that. And I was doing all right. This is only one day. I was doing okay until I called Helen, and as soon as I heard her voice, then that was it. I told her, 'Look, I don't feel any of the medication. I'm checking out.' And once she said yes—well, it was all over. I just checked out. And instead of turning my money into the cashier when I came in, I hadn't, I had kept it in my pants. So when we got our clothes back, I checked. I looked through my wallet, and it was there. So I guess that colored guy seen it and he went out ahead of me and must have went into the waiting room right outside, and he picked up two of these guys out of the waiting room, and said, 'Look here, this kid has a whole lot of money on him, let's take him off.'

"Now there was construction workers, white guys, working right there, people walking on the street. And now they see a nigger and two Spanish guys jump me, as small as I am and as big as they were, and they were 160 at the least, each one of them. And I think I was maybe, at the time, 110, 115—tops. And nobody even said, 'Hey, what are you doing?' They just stood there and watched the whole thing."

Bobby stopped talking. He chewed on his fingernails and stared out the window at the dark sky. The lights in the room were out and he sat silhouetted in the glow from the neon lights in Needle Park. After a few minutes I asked: "Do you and Helen fight a lot?"

"Do we fight a lot! We've had *some* fights. We didn't have any fights until maybe a year, a year and a half after we were going together—as far as I can remember it was something like that. We got along very good. Then we got into a couple of arguments. Oh, no, no, no. It wasn't a year and a half. What am I talking about? I come home January 4th from Comstock after doing twenty-eight months, and I met Helen through my brother in February. And I started going with her three days after I met her. Let's see, that was February, March—I got arrested April. I went to KY for five months. I come home November 1st, and before I even came home we had an argument through the mail and I didn't write her for about a month and a half. And when I came home, I flew home. She sent me plane fare and everything. And I went and got high before I even went home to see her. And I'm the one that was mad that night. She didn't say anything. She didn't argue.

"We were living in the Martell Hotel then, and one day we got into an argument, and I told her, 'Be quiet or I'll smack you in the face.' And she said, 'Go ahead, I dare you.' So I told her, 'Helen, say that one more time.' And she said it and I hit her.

"That was the first time I ever hit her. Oh, I smacked her and she fell on the couch, and Hank my brother and his wife were living with us then. We were taking care of them 'cause I was doing all right making a lot of money and Helen was making a lot of money. And like I must have blacked out. I got mad, I got that mad. And I black out sometimes, and I don't remember what I'm doing. And the next thing I remember was Hank was pulling me off her, and like her eyes were big and her tongue was hanging out of her mouth, and I was choking her. I was sitting on her, choking her. And I guess I tried to kill her. I don't remember. In fact the only thing I remember was smacking her and her falling on the couch. And I kind of like remember her calling my brother and then he pulled me off."

Chapter 8

"He was how I met her in the first place, my brother. When he first met his wife, Nancy, she and another girl were living in this hotel, and this other girl was a real scank. And I hadn't made it with any girls since I'd been home from jail that time. I've always been kind of shy of girls when I first meet them. Usually when I first meet people I'm very quiet. I sit and find out what kind of people they are before I even commit myself. Something happened that the two girls separated. The scank left and Nancy went with my brother. They knew Helen before that somehow, I don't know how. And they moved in with Helen. So I met my brother on the street one day and he gave me their phone number and the address. So, I think it was that day or the next day, I called up and told them I was coming down. And I came down. And I walked in the house, and Helen was in bed sleeping. And she woke up when I came in the house. So my brother brought me into the bedroom and says, 'Helen, this is Bobby, my brother I was telling you about.' And like the first words out of her mouth made me turn like blood red. She said, 'Oh yeah, but he's cuter than what you said he was.'

"Now I wasn't used to talk like that 'cause I'd been away in jail for three years and hadn't so much as kissed a girl. So like right away when I blushed she thought it was cute. She started teasing me. So we got along right away. We got along very good. So I wanted to get high. So I told my brother, I says, 'Hank, I want to get high.' So he says, 'No.' Now Helen's listening to this—it was before she started using, and like she was *death* on drugs. She was *death*. That's what Hank was doing there, in fact. She was trying to help him kick. And he had some stuff in the house and I knew it. So I told him, 'I want to get high.' He says, 'No.' And Helen says, 'No, Hank, don't give him any.' So I said, 'To hell with you, I got money in my pocket. I know where to score. I'll see you later.' So I started going out the door and Hank said, 'Look, Helen, I don't want him taking it by himself and maybe OD'ing.' So, after she thought about it, she said, 'All right.' So I got high. And then I left. Helen was talking to Hank and I was leaving. And I says so long to Hank, so long to Nancy, and I turned around to Helen and I told her, 'Helen,

I like you. You're real people.' 'Cause like every hooker I've ever met—I've never made it with a hooker before. Like when you walk into the house and they first meet you, they start talking $100 bills, $500 bills. They're trying, I don't know—they're phonies. A lot of them are, not all of them. And like she was regular people, like for real. That's what it was that I liked about her. So maybe two, three days pass, and I was going to the house regular 'cause right away I liked her.

"This was about three years ago. Now Hank told me she was pretty, and I hadn't seen her with any make-up on 'cause she hadn't gotten out of bed that first day I was there. So the second day I come downtown and they weren't home. So I walked into this restaurant here in Needle Park and they were sitting in the back. And she had black slacks on and a black jacket and a black scarf. And they were all sitting at a table and I stopped and—it was raining out and I had an umbrella in my hand—and I looked at her and I looked to my brother Hank, and I says, 'Hank, you told me she was pretty.' And like I could see that she was starting to get insulted, probably thinking like I was going to say she was ugly. Then I say, 'But she's not pretty, she's beautiful.' And she didn't know how to act behind that, and neither did I after I said it. I was hung up for words. I started to turn red again.

"The same day we went out and started running through the rain. My brother Hank was yelling and singing and all that kind of stuff. Well, then we wound up in the drugstore across from the restaurant—right over there. You can see it from here. And there was an iron, you know, one of those clothes irons, maybe four inches, and they wanted $7 for it. So my brother said, 'Helen, for a couple more dollars, you could get a big steam iron.' She says, 'Yeah, but I like it, I want it.' And like I liked that too. And he tells her for a couple of more dollars she could get a steam iron. But she says, 'But this is nice. I like it. It's cute. I want it.' And he says something else, and she says, 'Well, I'm going to get it.' So, like I like that. I went for the way she came on with it. So it stuck in my mind. I like people that if they want something they'll get it. I'm like that way myself. If I can't buy it, I'll steal it. If I can't steal it, I'll get it some way. If possible.

"Anyway, she got the iron and we went to her place on 71st Street. So nothing happened that night and I went home. The next night I come back and there are a lot of people in the house. Al came over, he'd just come home from jail, and a couple of other people. Before they came over, it was me, Helen, Hank, and Nancy and somebody else. I forgot who it was. Anyway, Nancy, Hank, and this other person, they went out. Now my hand had accidently bumped against Helen's arm, and her skin was *so* smooth, like I was fascinated by it. It was like silk. So I just put my hand on her arm and I started stroking it. I had gotten off and I was high, and I was more or less goofing on it. You know how pillowcases are smooth, like I'll lay there and play with it in my hands. Like I like smooth things like nylons and things like that.

"So anyway, I started rubbing her arm. Then I started

rubbing her back. And my brother came home with Nancy. So anyway, I got completely hung up on the smoothness of her skin, and then all these other people come over. Maybe they stayed over two hours. So Helen must have got tired or something. 'Cause she said, 'Okay, everybody has to go, I'm going to sleep.' So I started to put my coat on. I figured she meant me too. And I was on parole anyway. You know, I had to be home at certain times. So I started to put my coat on and my brother comes over to me and says, 'Bobby, take your coat off. Helen says she wants you to stay.' So I tell him, 'Look, Hank, I'm on parole.' I've only been home three weeks, maybe two or three weeks. I says, 'I can't be staying out now.' I says, 'If the PO goes over to the house, it's going to be all over.'

"So anyway, all he had to do was say it one more time. He said, 'Helen wants you to stay.' That was it. I took my coat off. That night . . . now, remember, I hadn't touched a girl for about twenty-eight, twenty-nine months . . . We wound up with Hank and Nancy in one bed and Helen and I in the other. And I hadn't touched a girl for *so* long. And she probably expected me to make advances at her. But all I'd do—her back was toward me—was kind of rub my hand on her back like I had done earlier. And I let her go to sleep, and I went to sleep.

"The next night the same thing happened, and I knew she couldn't figure it out. She could *not* figure it out. She maybe thought I was a fag or something. The third night I was lying in bed. Everybody else was still up. I was dressed, lying in bed dressed. She came in the room, closed the door, and she said something like, 'I can't understand you.' Then something happened, like that's the first time we like made it together. And like, I told her maybe four or five days later, I told her, 'Helen, don't start liking me too much, whatever you do. 'Cause once I find myself liking you too much, I'm going to get up and leave.' Like before I went upstate I went with this girl Ann three years. We broke up and I made a complete fool out of myself trying to get her back. I begged her and pleaded with her to go back with me—this, that, and the other thing—a real jerk I made out of myself. Then the whole two years I did upstate nothing was on my mind but this girl Ann. And I thought I was madly in love with her. And like I told Helen about it. I told her I had like a mental block in my mind that I didn't think anybody could break. That I had a brick wall—that's what I told her it was.

"And a couple of days after I told her that, I said to her, 'Helen, I don't know what's the matter, but I think the cement between these bricks is weakening 'cause brick by brick it's being torn down'—or something like that. 'And as each brick gets lower, I can start to see you standing behind the wall.' Like, in other words, she's starting to get to me. So she told me the same thing—like with her, like I was getting to her. So now I'm afraid that if I go for her, I'll get hurt again like I did the last time. And I was afraid.

"Two days later we made love again, and I didn't say nothing to her. We made love and she told me she loved me . . . during the sex. I didn't say anything. I was, you know, too shy. The next day I went to work, and I used to call her every lunch hour and every break. I was an elevator operator. I was making $87 a week. So I called her up the next day, and she had been a little high that day too, the night before. And I asked her—I says, 'Helen,' and she says, 'Yeah,' and I says, 'Do you remember last night what happened?' She says, 'Yeah.' I says, 'Do you remember what you said?' And she paused for a minute. Then she says, 'Yeah, I remember.' And I says, 'Did you mean it, or was it just out of a passion?' She says, 'I meant it.' She says, 'Why?' I told her I wanted to be sure. She said, 'Well, how do you feel?' I tell her I feel happy, and that was it. Ever since then, we've been together. She wasn't using drugs then either, and she was some beautiful girl. I used to walk the streets and people used to look at her twice. Boy, she was a doll. She's still got a beautiful body even when she's strung out. Like if she's not sick, and she puts her make-up on and the right clothes, even a skirt and a blouse, it's hard to tell that she's hooked. Like just before she went into the hospital, for some strange reason she used to eat at least a meal a day and she started gaining weight, and she never really got like some of these girls who get skinny—like I get skinny. I go down to nothing, like 110 pounds. And when I kick I go down to 93 or even lower. Like she doesn't look like a junky. Like if you didn't know she was a junky, a lot of people wouldn't know it.

"So anyway, when I first started going with her, right away it was one of those things. Like in a week I found myself telling her that I was in love with her. Same thing with her. And I didn't want that. Like I told you before,

I was afraid. And she didn't want it because she was afraid. She had been going with this girl for three years. And like I was starting to get another problem with drugs, like I was starting to get high every day. And she had a problem with her own mind—not sure whether she wanted to go with girls or with boys. So like she was very unsure of herself, very insecure. And like we both seemed to have a problem. Like I don't know. I don't know how to explain the way it was with her. She was afraid that it wouldn't work out and she was afraid that she was gay—that's what the whole thing was actually with her. She wasn't sure of herself. And I started going with her, and I'm the only . . . from what she tells me . . . like she had been married before she went with this girl, and she tells me that even counting when she was married, I'm the only one that ever made her reach a climax, the only *man* that ever made her reach a climax. And that she was very, very unsure of herself.

"And eventually she found out like she wasn't gay. Like I kept telling her she was too much of a woman to even come anywhere near it. And like she was always afraid, and then, I don't know, as time went on, she realized like she loved me. Not just loved me but was in love with me. Like it was me and only me. First, last, and always. And like ever since then, like everything was like real sweet.

"So anyway, she was hooking when I met her. So I didn't go for that at all. 'Cause I hadn't never made it with a hooker before. So one night she had a date, so she told me to come back late, in an hour or something like that.

And I came back in an hour, an hour and fifteen minutes, something like that. I came back later than I was supposed to. I ring the bell and walk through the front door and was going to the apartment, and the door opened and she had the chain on it and she stuck her hand out like. And I stopped dead, right in the hallway. I don't know if I wanted to cry, run, kick the door in. I didn't know *what* I wanted to do. And she must have seen the expression on my face. We've talked about that a lot of times. Like I was *so* hurt. Ever since that time, every time she'd go out with a trick I'd get an attitude. Or if the trick would come over I'd be sulky, nasty with the trick. Even today, I don't like her hustling. I'd rather have her stay home and I got to go out and steal.

"I don't think you or anybody else can understand the way I felt standing in the hallway, like the only person I really loved in there with someone else. And like stopping me from coming in. I don't know. I didn't want to go back any more. And she knew something was the matter 'cause she could see the expression on my face or something. Even today when we get to talking, like that always comes up. I've never liked her to hook. Like a lot of times I tell her, 'Don't go out. Stop hooking. Get a job.' She just never got to stop.

"She has to have me like to lean on. She has to have somebody to lean on. With little problems she'd come to me. She'd cry in her sleep. She'd wake up crying. If somebody would wake her up too hard, she'd cry. I don't know, she's very timid in a lot of ways. It's hard to explain. I just never liked her to hook. She used to make like at least $1,500 in one week, $1,500 the next week, maybe more the next week. Even with that money coming in and most of it going on clothes for me and things like that—she was buying nothing but the best . . . $50 sweaters, $75 cuff links, suits, everything . . . nothing but the best she used to get me— and even with that, I would have rather give that up than have her go out with other guys. Even today, like she's got two habits to support. I don't do anything. Like the last run I had was fifteen months, the last time before I got busted for procuring. If I went out twenty times in that fifteen months to make money, that was a lot. She made it all. She supported both our habits all this time. I don't contribute anything. Except another problem, another habit to support. And my love for her, that's all. We're just together. Like it was even me who got her started on drugs. Like I didn't mean to or want to or anything like that but like it's just the way it happened. Like here's how it happened.

"I was home and this kid I was upstate with, we used to have a singing group up there. We used to always sing. We'd sing practically half the bit away. And he was over at the house that night, and Helen had a toothache. And it was really—I mean, it was out of sight—it was too much. She was going crazy with it. And I was just cooking up, ready to get off. And I think it was a Sunday night. There was no drugstores open. There was no dentists—nothing for the pain. So something happened that it came up to give her a little bit of the stuff. For maybe fifteen minutes to a half hour, for maybe more, I argued with him, 'No, no, no, no,' and like at first she said no, no, no. But this guy kept talking about it and talking about it, trying to get me to give it to her. Not that he wanted to start her on a drug or anything, but he just wanted to see her get out of the pain 'cause she was really dying with that pain. So finally, from hearing him saying it'll take the pain away, kill the pain, she just wanted that pain gone so bad, she started asking me for it.

"So finally I gave in. She started crying, and I can't, even still today, I can't see her cry. If she starts to cry, I tell her, 'Helen, stop crying.' I get mad. I don't like to see her cry. So I gave her a couple of drops, and that was it. That's when we were living in the Cheshire too—doing terrific. She was bringing home maybe, never less than $150, $200 every day. And that was only one trick, maybe two. She had only $100 tricks, mostly, and $50 tricks. I was spending maybe close to $100 every day, not that I had to, but it was just what I was spending on myself, plus I was giving my brother Hank maybe half of what I got. Maybe a little more, maybe 75 percent worth, plus you know, what I got myself. Plus paying $75 a week rent. Plus we were paying for Hank's rent. Plus food and everything like that. So like we were going for maybe, who knows, $1,500 a week. And she was making more than that. We always had money. I always had $150, $200, $300 in my pocket.

"So after a while I got really strung out again and I went to KY. And I was there maybe a month or something like that and when I got home she was staying at a nice hotel.

I'd gotten off right away on a Dilaudid 'cause I didn't want to use stuff. She gave me an argument on stuff, so I settled for Dilaudid. We went to the bedroom, and we were lying down talking. And out of nowhere, she says, 'Bobby, I'm hooked.' I looked at her and says, 'What do you mean, you're hooked?' She says, 'I've been using stuff for the past six months.' Now, before I went to KY I stayed *so* high, with my eyes closed all the time, laying down. I guess I never expected it of her, so I never looked for it. I never looked at her eyes to see if they were pinned. I don't know how I felt when she told me that. But I felt so empty. Like I wanted to get up and bash her brains against the wall. And then I felt sorry for her, and then later on I found out from people that she went around asking people the fastest way to get a habit, thinking that when I come home from KY, if I see her hooked, I'll see what it's doing to her and stay off myself. Like she was trying to use psychology on me. But it didn't work and she's been using stuff ever since then. And it's been really tough for her. I mean like working, it makes it a lot harder for her to work, to hustle, since she's on junk. And like I worry about her 'cause of some of these creeps she turns tricks with. So when she used to go out on dates, like from her books—she had whole filing drawers full of books and index cards on all her dates, you know, even with what they talked about on the last date, so when she saw the guy again, no matter how long it had been, she could bring up the same subject and ask him about it and make him think like he was the only one she really remembered, really cared about. So anyway

when she used to go out on those dates—a hundred dollars,
two hundred dollars—like it was real safe. They're not the
kind of guys are gonna knock her around or decide they
want to get their kicks by beating her up or something.
But when she started on drugs and lost her looks, and
started working on the street, like if I was around, I would
never let her go with a trick if possible without me guard-
ing her. I'd wait outside the hotel, wait downstairs in case
something happened. 'Cause I've known a lot of girls who
got beat up, robbed, and what not.

"So one night she goes up to the Martell Hotel, this
hotel we're in. She gets in the door of the guy's room. Two
minutes later, I had that funny feeling that something was
wrong. She had told me to wait in the restaurant, but I
went up anyway. All of a sudden I hear, 'Bobby!' and I
hear, 'Smack!' I hear, 'Bobby, Bobby!' So I took the nozzle off, you know the fire hose in the hallway, and she had
gotten the door open and she was struggling with the guy.
And he had smacked her. Right away I knew that it was
him who had smacked her 'cause, like, you know, she
wouldn't swing out on somebody like that. So I ran in and
I could see that they were like struggling. Like I didn't
want to run in swinging this thing—like I might hit her.
So I run in and I get between them and I give the guy a
shove. So he fell down on the bed. So I didn't have to hit
him with the nozzle. So I jump on top of him and I grab
him and I smack him a couple of times. And like I started
going berserk like. 'You hit my girl!' and I'd smack him.
'You hit my girl!' And now Helen's starting with 'Bobby,

stop it, stop it!' So I told her, 'Okay.' And I told him, 'You're going to pay for this,' and like I had went through his pockets while I was sitting on him.

"Like that's the only incident like that that happened. It was a minor one, really. If I had hit him with that nozzle, I would have really . . . like it was a heavy nozzle.

"So if she has any kind of trouble I go fight with whoever it is. Like somebody made a remark at her, this guy, Louie. Like I had told her a couple of times, 'If I ever had a fight with Louie I'd break his jaw.' I used that expression, 'I'd break his jaw.' Like though I was so strung out, and he was so healthy. He wasn't a junkie. She said, 'Bobby, he'd wipe the streets with you, let's face it. He's healthy, and look at you.' So I told her, 'Helen, don't underestimate me, that's where people make their mistake. They always underestimate me 'cause I'm small.' So this guy made a mistake by underestimating me. I took him outside the restaurant and I belted him. So when I hit him, he got so scared. Like he put his two arms around my waist. And his head was about near my chest. And like I was just standing there, throwing uppercuts at his face. And like the cops came over and broke it up. And when she heard about it, she never underestimated me no more."

Chapter 9

"I don't know why, but like I'm very nervous. Like for example I walk fast, and like if somebody's in front of me, I get very, very aggravated with them. I'll shoot around them—like I'll walk in front of them and get mad, and I might say something under my breath or I might say, 'Move it the hell out of the way.' I might say it. What I mean is, I don't like people. I can't get along with square people. Maybe if I got back off drugs and got a job, I might try to force it from myself. Maybe in a week or two it'll just come back. It'll most likely come back, but I just have to get it started again. Like, even other junkies I don't like. I wouldn't put my money in a junkie's hand unless I really

really trusted him. In fact, Hank, my own brother, took money from me. Now, if my brother's going to turn around and beat me, who can I trust? I can't trust nobody out there. The only one I trust is Helen. And even she's like at times gotten off behind my back. Like how many times I've stayed sixteen, seventeen, eighteen hours and she disappeared some place, and I know she's not going to go that long without a fix. She can tell me anything she wants, but I know Helen. And she'll come back and tell me she hasn't gotten off—and she's high. Like a couple of times she's been gone all day and all night and I didn't see her until the next day, and if I didn't do anything, I'd be sick when she came back. But when she came back she'd have a bag of stuff to get me straight, and I'd get off first, before I even start arguing with her.

"And I beat people for their money now too, but that's what using junk does to you 'cause I wasn't always like that. But now I could go out in the street and beat somebody, steal something, and it doesn't bother me. But like when I hear of a junkie that he'll kill his mother or shoot his brother, I don't even keep conversation with people that think like that, 'cause they're ignorant, they believe everything they read. Like newspapers, the way they write things up, it's ten times and a half worse than it really is. They exaggerate. Like this girl gave me money to score for her. Now I went up to the connection's house, and I sat there an hour and a half, and this girl when she gave me the money she was very sick, and I stayed up there an hour and a half. Now when I come back she was gone.

She thought I'd beat her. Like I was sick myself when I went up there. In fact I was so far gone I was like sort of going through withdrawal. That's how sick I was. For an hour and a half, being sick with her stuff in my pocket, I went out looking for her and I gave her her stuff. And she turned around and she straightened me out. When she started telling people in the neighborhood about it, they couldn't believe it. But like I said, I do con people out of their money, beat them for it . . . and I guess I con myself a lot too, and a lot of other people. I don't mean just for their money but for other things. Like kicking. I've said to people I was gonna kick to satisfy them, to make them happy like when they write me letters when I'm in jail. 'Please, Bobby, don't do this and don't do that.' Before Helen used drugs, she used to write the same thing, and I used to write her, 'Okay, when I come home I won't use.' It was just that I couldn't be able to explain it to them, try to explain it to them. So they couldn't understand. So I would write to them and satisfy them by telling them, 'Okay, I won't use again.' And then when I got home, I would try to explain it, and wind up using again. It's disgusting, but it's just the way things are. Like I said I'm always very nervous and when I come home from jail I'm even worse. Like now I'm very irritated. I don't know why. I guess it's my fault. I don't know. Like the last time I came home from jail, before this time, I was nasty, very nasty. Same thing this time. And like I don't like myself like this. I don't understand myself like this. Like today . . . no, when was it? . . . Anyway, the last time I was with her, Helen, she woke up sick. She had given somebody $25. She wanted to surprise me by coming home with the stuff instead of coming home and giving me the money and having me go out and get it. She wanted to surprise me by waking me up and saying, 'Here, Bobby,' and just let me get off in bed. That's what she used to do . . . wake me up and have my fix ready, like breakfast in bed. She wanted to surprise me. She gave the guy $25 to score for her. He went uptown. This was nine o'clock in the morning. At nine o'clock at night, we finally found out where he lives and we go up there. And he says, 'Look, I don't know how to tell you, but I got beat.' Now that's twelve hours we're waiting for him. He could have called and we could have went out and got some money. So we didn't get straight until about three o'clock this morning. And my last shot before that was close to maybe eighteen hours, twenty hours, something like that. It was a long time. Now she woke up very sick. She had a *bombita* and a $3 bag. And she started putting it in the cooker. I told her, 'Leave half of it in the cooker for me.' Now we'd be lucky if two three-dollar bags would straighten either one of us out, the way stuff is out there now, never mind one, never mind half of one. Like she looked at me like I was crazy. She said, 'Bobby, it's only a three-dollar bag.' I says, 'I know what it is, leave half of it for me.'

"She says, 'Bobby!' She started crying. She says, 'Bobby, I'm sick. Please let me do it and I'll go out and get some money, fast. I'll turn a trick or something. I'll go see Farrell, and borrow. I can get money faster if I'm straight,' which is true. I would probably have got straight in an hour. I was like cold-blooded. I told her, 'I don't want to hear no stories. Leave half in the cooker, or I'm going to take it all.' And that's just what I told her. And like, I don't know. It's not like me to do something like that. I did the same thing the last time I came home. I don't know why. There's a reason behind it. That's vengeance, some kind of vengeance. I'm very spiteful. Like if I have an argument with somebody, and they bite me on my big toe, you *know* eventually I'm going to get to their big toe and bite it back. I'm very spiteful like that. It scares me. Especially with Helen. If it was somebody else, I wouldn't care. But with her, who's supposed to mean so much to me, that I could do something like that and threaten to take the whole thing, knowing that neither one of us are going to get straight, not even on a whole one, maybe just get the edges taken off, enough to feel good enough to go out. But to do what I did. If I'm going to keep that up, she can get somebody a whole lot better than me. If I kept that up, I wouldn't be any good to myself.

"Like a couple days ago, I scored two $3 bags. I had to pay $6 apiece for them, but they were better than any $5 bag they're selling uptown for $7. I scored them, I gave them to Helen. We had a *bombita*. Like I told you, I'm using too many bombitas. Like they make me feel bugs crawl over me. I pick my face and hands all day. I actually *see* bugs. And like she drops the *bombita*. I didn't care 'cause I have more at home. I said let's go back to the Martell and get off there with a *bombita*. She didn't want to.

So she started walking up the steps of the connection's house and I says, 'Helen, come here.' I was going to try to talk her into going to the hotel. She got scared. She starts running up the stairs. And her being afraid of me like that, that got me so mad. Like there were two vice-squad cops right on the same floor where I walked out of the connection's house with stuff. And I seen them there. And I just gave a scream: 'Helen, get back here!' It was loud in the hallway, and it was echoing. She ran. She ran up to the sixth floor as sick as she was, ran in the bathroom and locked the door, and tried to hide from me. You do something like that with an animal. You hide from an animal.

"I told her about four times to open the door. She wouldn't open it. And I threatened to kick the panel out the next time I asked her, and she finally opened it. And she was like in the shower stall, crouched down, like a real refugee. You see them picture posters of refugees crouched down, and the *fear* that she had on her face, and the shaking . . . she was actually, really shaking, she couldn't hold the cooker steady. I tell you, I'll leave her for good before I keep her going through that. If there's some way of putting her in Bellevue or some place like that, I'll make her go. I don't want her to be afraid. But after what I just said now, what I been saying, how much I care for the girl, I might go out there, find her some place, get high on a *bombita* and get into an argument, and throw all kinds of punches at her. I don't know, I don't know why. Each time I hit her, she comes back to me. One time after I beat her so bad, this is a couple of days before I got busted the last time, I hit her in the kidneys with a telephone. I threw punches at her. I really gave her a beating. After I came to my senses, I was lying in bed, thinking of all I did, feeling all kinds of sorry about it. She came over to me. She told me *she* was sorry. I don't think anything can make me feel lower than she can. She knows how to make me feel good, she knows how to make me feel bad."

Bobby stopped talking and just sat there slouched in the chair, biting his nails, looking out the window. He was silent, thoughtful for three or four minutes, and then he said, as if making at last a final, this-time-for-sure decision on a matter that had long defied resolution:

"But I'm through with drugs. I have a little chippy now since I got out of jail but I want to clean up. I want to get a job. I want to be square again. I hang around Needle Park here 'cause I just don't have anywhere else to go. That's it in a nutshell. No place else to go. Except upstate with my parents. And that's murder, man, that's murder. 'Bobby, where are you going? Bobby, stay home. Bobby don't come home late. Bobby do this, Bobby do that, Bobby that's not the right girl.' So I get another girl. *She's* not the right girl. 'Why don't you go back with Ann?' 'You just finished telling me she's not the right girl.' That's why I can't live with my family. My life's not my own when I'm with them. That's funny. Like my life is my own here in Needle Park. My life belongs to junk. But I'm giving it up. Like Monday I'm going upstate and kick for good. I'm tired of this life. I've had it. I know I could make it out there without junk. And like if I can't make the square life, if I find it too rough for me, which I doubt, the stuff will always be on the corners, the connections will always be there. It's been there for hundreds of years, and it'll be there for another hundred years. I can always get it if I want it. But I can kick and be square. Just as long as I don't try to throw it all up ahead of me, like 'Okay, I'm not going to use it no more and forget it.' Can't do that, 'cause you're going to find yourself using again. The best way I figured out, like I thought about a lot of ways, and the only way I can figure out is get up in the morning and wash, get dressed, comb your hair, and say, 'Bobby, not today. I'll get high tomorrow.' And the next day, the same thing. Day by day. After a while, you wake up in the morning, you come home that night, look at that mirror and realize you forgot to tell yourself, 'Not today.' And after a while you don't got to do it no more. I've had it. I'm through."

Another long silence.

"Bobby, how long has it been right now since you've had a shot?"

"Two or three hours, maybe."

"How long do you think it will be till you get off again?"

"Maybe right after I leave here."

"Well, then, why do you say that you've had it with drugs?"

"Well, after Monday anyway."

book two

Chapter 10

In the next couple of weeks the panic came on full blast, and heroin was almost unobtainable. What there was in Needle Park was coming from Bobby. He had gone through with his plans to go into business for himself, and for reasons I could not then imagine, Little Tony was letting him get away with it.

Bobby's business wasn't great, but not from lack of demand. When the other junkies found out he was dealing, they started hounding him night and day. "You got stuff, Bobby, baby? When you gettin' some stuff, man? Like don't forget your friends, baby, I mean you remember that time you were up real tight and I used to give you tastes of mine, remember, baby?" But Bobby was having a tough time getting stuff. He could have made a fortune, he told me, if it weren't for the panic. "With this panic, man, you just can't get the stuff to sell. I mean there just ain't no stuff around. Sometimes I can't even get enough to keep myself straight, let alone Helen. But if there weren't a panic, if there *weren't*, man, I'd be so rich, *so* rich."

Once in a while a shipment came through and then he could talk a couple of pieces out of Santo. How, I couldn't figure out. Why was Santo—Little Tony's cutter—dealing pieces to Bobby when the stuff was so hard to get and Little Tony must have wanted everything he could lay his hands on? I couldn't figure it out. But anyway Bobby wasn't getting enough to grow rich on. Sometimes not even enough to keep Helen straight. He was always straight, but when he had stuff and was dealing he had to act sick in front of Helen so she wouldn't know he was dealing instead of giving it to her.

Then a shipment described by Bobby as "really big" came down from Harlem (Bobby said they had the stuff stockpiled up there since before the panic and were letting it out slow to make it last and to keep the price up) and Bobby went to see Santo to get as many pieces of it as he could. He asked me to go along. I was surprised. I had been wondering for some time why Bobby and Helen were so unsuspicious of me. They bought and sold drugs in front of me—committing felonies that could get them up to fifteen years if I turned out to be a cop—without a hint of apprehension. They had for the most part stopped trying to con me out of money, so I was no longer sure why they were letting me hang around, even encouraging me to stay with them. (On one occasion, in fact, they had actually complained when I left them for a day to go home and rest. "Where were you, man?" they asked when I returned. "I mean, that's not very nice, you know, just taking off like that, and anyway you really missed a lot. Billy took an OD and we had to work for two hours on him. You should'a been here.") I finally got an answer from a psychiatrist who had worked with addicts at the Lexington hospital. The way junkies lived, he told me, their egos took a tremendous beating. A relationship with a square gave their dignity a boost. They could feel above him. They could savor the reversal of the teacher-student, judge-defendant, do-gooder-addict, cop-prisoner relationship they had always known. For once they were the figures of authority. For the first time, they were on the front end of the hyphen, and the square was the student.

So I found myself at 3 a.m. with Bobby in a cab heading down Second Avenue for Santo's apartment on the Lower East Side. It wasn't really his apartment, I discovered when we got there, only his cutting room, where he and his assistants collected to cut up quarter kilos into ounces and, for an extra charge, to cut the ounces into bags for relatively smalltime pushers like Bobby who didn't want the bother of cutting their own pieces.

We stopped on Stanton Street, dark and scattered with trash and garbage. The buildings were all low—three or four stories—and falling down. In the darkness, the square

hulking shapes looked like rows of great brown beasts, now
dead and decomposing, the flesh flaking off into the streets
and alleys around them. The smells as we emerged from
the cab supported this image.

Bobby and I entered an open hallway with mailboxes
hanging off the cracked walls, and walked on back forty
feet, past a half dozen overflowing garbage cans, to a door.
Bobby pulled the door open and led the way up filthy,
broken stairs lighted on each landing by a bare bulb. We
climbed all the way to the fourth floor and knocked on a
door. Someone knocked back and Bobby knocked again,
this time in a coded rhythm. The door opened a half inch
and Bobby whispered something through the crack. Then
it went just wide enough to let the two of us in. Inside,
the room was huge. The left half, after we entered the door,
faded off into darkness. At the far end I could see the dim
outlines of a grand piano. Waist-high bookcases filled with
dust-covered paperbacks lined all the walls, and above the
bookcases were windows completely and permanently covered by blankets nailed to the walls. On the right, in what
had once been a kitchen, was a large table spread completely with black cloth covered by a sheet of plate glass.

Three men in white surgical masks worked around the
table. Here the light was brilliant, almost blinding. A few
glassine bags about the size of a man's palm were piled on
one end of the table. In front of each masked worker were
mounds of white powder and piles of small, stamp-sized
glassine envelopes.

Bobby and Santo went off into the dark end of the room

for a moment, and I saw Bobby take something out of his shirt. He had managed a buy. They came back into the light and Bobby introduced Santo. He had a large round fat face with a tiny fish mouth and too-small ears lying flat against his head. He wore a gray checked suit with a red tie and a red handkerchief in the breast pocket. He was about twenty-eight and effusively friendly, greeting me as he might a guest at a cocktail party.

"Bobby says you're interested in all this," Santo said. "Want me to explain things?" It was clear he feared nothing from me.

I said I would like him to explain. His business was wholesale heroin, but he was as casual as a Westchester banker showing someone around his new greenhouse.

"The men wear those masks," Santo started, "to keep from breathing junk that gets into the air. If they didn't wear the masks and worked here long enough they'd get high on the stuff and then after a while they'd get a regular habit. And we certainly wouldn't want that." He smiled at Bobby and Bobby smiled back, a little uncertainly, not sure if he had been insulted or not.

"The different piles there," Santo went on, pointing as he spoke, "are heroin, quinine, and milk sugar. We work a four-to-one cut here—about four parts of milk sugar or quinine to one part heroin. Actually, of course, the heroin has already been cut way down before we even get it. So the guy on the street gets maybe five percent. The quinine is just to cut the sweet taste of the sugar. Heroin itself has a bitter taste and if a junkie tastes some stuff before he uses it and it's real sweet he figures he's bought a blank and gets upset. So we put in the quinine to make it bitter. The rest is pretty much obvious. You can see how it works just by watching. Any questions, just ask. That guy over there is gonna cut Bobby's stuff now."

Bobby had managed to get three pieces out of Santo, and one of the men started cutting it. He took a wire coat hanger that had been spread open and covered with nylon from a stocking, and put it in front of him on the glass-topped table. Then he opened one of the ounce envelopes and carefully emptied the contents onto the nylon. He lifted the coat-hanger-and-nylon sieve and shook it gently, sifting the heroin through the nylon onto the table. He shook it slowly, almost tenderly, taking great care not to let the sifted heroin spread too much. When he was through, the heroin sat in a high fluffy mound, almost twice the volume he had started with. He took a razor blade and carefully scraped the heroin that had drifted away from the edge of the mound back toward the center. Next he took a whisky shot glass, filled it once with heroin, and emptied it onto the coat-hanger-nylon sifter. He added two shots each of milk sugar and quinine. He mixed the chemicals together on the nylon, then sifted the whole mess again.

Now everyone pitched in. The three men at the table and Santo and Bobby each took baby measuring spoons and dipped them into the mound of cut heroin. When each had a spoonful, he leveled it off with a razor blade and dumped it in a neat pile on the glass. After they had about ten piles, one of the men started shoveling each pile into one of the stamp-sized bags. Everyone else measured, and the one man bagged. When everything was in bags, Bobby and Santo started folding them over and sealing them shut with Scotch tape. The others went to work on Bobby's second and third ounces. Finally everything was cut and all the bags were rubber-banded together in bundles of twenty-five bags each. Hundreds and hundreds of bundles were stacked up on the table. Each bundle would sell for $75—and sell as easily as water in hell.

"Nice business, huh?" Santo said.

"Nice business," I said.

"Come on, man," Bobby said, "We—I—got work to do. Let's go." He scooped the bundles into four large manila envelopes and one small one. When we got down to the street Bobby walked ten steps up the block and turned into an alley. I groped along behind him in the dark. Bobby stopped, reached up over his head, and loosened five bricks in the wall. He took them out, stuffed the large manila envelopes in the opening, and replaced the bricks. "Now let's beat it," he said nervously, and we walked quickly down to Delancey Street and hailed a cab. We got out at 72nd Street and Broadway.

"The thing is," Bobby said, still carrying the small envelope, "you got to stash the stuff as fast as you can, so if you're taken off or busted you don't lose everything. You can still always go back to the stash and get what's left after you get out of jail. 'Cause like you know you're going to get bail, right?, and like if you have to go on trial you're going to need that stuff to raise the money for a good lawyer and for . . . like if he has to pay someone off or something."

As we walked down Broadway, Bobby moved fast, darting ferret-like up and down sidestreets, into hallways, stores, alleyways, phone booths. He was everywhere, and by the time we had reached 70th Street the manila envelope was empty. The bundles had disappeared, one or two at a time, behind radiators, under trash cans, on top of phone booths, in back of fire extinguishers. "Now," he said, sitting down in the dark on a bench in Needle Park, "business *really* starts. And it's perfectly safe, right? Like here I am, clean as anything, nothing on me. I just sit here. Watch."

He was right. People started coming up and sitting down next to him. Most of them I had never seen before. They passed money to him in the dark, and I caught phrases like, ". . . trash can 71st and Amsterdam . . . phone booth, Digby's Drugs . . . radiator south entrance Talbot Hotel . . ." It went on like that for two hours. Finally Bobby got up.

"Walk with me over to the Talbot, will you? I gotta get a room, and having a respectable guy like you with me won't hurt." He smiled. "And then, too, having you with me might help keep me from getting taken off with all this loot." At that moment Bobby had more money on him than I had ever seen at any one time in my entire life. And there was more—lots, lots more—behind some bricks in an alley on Stanton Street.

Chapter 11

The Talbot was a tiny, seedy hotel sandwiched between more respectable hotels on West 72nd Street across from a row of high-rent apartment houses. It was not quite so filthy or run down as the hotels nearer Needle Park, and to Bobby it represented a step up. But status was not its only advantage. It had a night-desk man who in less panicky times would send heroin to the room faster than you could get a ham on rye from room service at the Hilton.

When a junkie has a hotel room, the word spreads fast. All his friends and their friends stream in and the place turns into a shooting gallery. I knocked on the door of Bob and Helen's room several nights after the heroin cutting session, and Bobby let me in. The room was littered with the debris of addiction—bits of toilet paper and clothing that had been used to wipe blood from arms; glasses half filled with water tinted red from the cleaning of many needles; scraps of electric-light cord chopped up and separated into thin strands with which to unclog needles; charred metal bottle tops used for cookers. Everywhere on the floor—strewn so thick you could not see the carpet—were clothing, old comic books, and cigarette butts. Sheets and blankets, cigarette holes burned in them by nodding addicts, had fallen from the bed and lay kicked into corners. Stuffing oozed from a waffle-sized burn in the mattress. The smell was of sweat and smoke and heroin.

Helen looked worse than I had ever seen her. Her eyes were widely dilated, partly from heroin withdrawal, partly from enormous doses of barbiturates. She had a $50 date with a John in New Jersey, and Bobby and his friends were trying desperately to get her into shape for the trip. She was nearly unconscious. Two men held her up, and another whose name was Whitey brushed her hair for her. "Come on, Helen," Whitey pleaded, "you got to make that train. You got to get out there, baby. You can't miss this trick. Helen, you got to make it." She mumbled and slouched in her supporters' arms, and Whitey kept brushing.

Bobby walked over to a corner of the room that was stacked high with cases of coffee and cellophane packages of hair curlers. He and a friend had spotted a truck unloading supplies onto a sidewalk in front of a grocery store.

They had grabbed everything they could carry, and ran with it in their arms to the hotel. Now they were going to try to sell the haul. Remembering Bobby's wealth a couple of days earlier, I found this hard to understand. I took Bobby aside. "How come you're boosting hair curlers when you've got all that money from the junk?" I asked.

Bobby gave his sheepish, little-boy smile. "I got taken off," he said, embarrassed as a high-school freshman who has just seen a senior walk away with his girl. "Somebody grabbed the loot outa here that night and then when I went downtown again the stuff was gone from the alley, you know, from behind where the bricks were there in the alley." He stopped smiling. "Somebody must have followed me. Santo, maybe. Or one of Santo's guys. One of them. But I'll get them. I'll even it up. You can bet on that, you can bet on that." He lifted the edge of his sport shirt, which was hanging outside his trousers, and I looked down at his belt. The butt end of a pistol stuck out between the flesh and the waistband next to the buckle. "That's not gonna happen again," Bobby said. He looked down himself at the gun, then covered it again with the shirt. "Even Hank don't carry a piece," he said quietly. He paused for several seconds, pensive, and then suddenly came to life. "So anyway, that's where it's at. Easy come, easy go."

Easy come, easy go—thousands of dollars, tens of thousands. Bobby—all the junkies—had no idea at all what money was, any amount of it, hundreds or thousands or millions. Nothing meant anything but junk. If a sick junkie desperate for stuff knew there was a $5 bag under his bed and a $1,ooo bill outside under a trash can, he'd go for the $5 bag, shoot it up, go on a nod, and *then*—when he needed another nickel bag—go after the thousand. So here was Bobby, a rich man two days ago, now trying to hustle some stolen coffee and hair curlers.

The men who had been holding Helen up sat her on the bed. She fell back, anesthetized by the barbiturates. Someone knocked on the door and Bobby yelled at the men, "There's too much noise in here! Can't you guys shut up? That's probably the cops now. You make so much racket they could hear you inside the station house." He walked to the door and whispered, "Who is it?"

"It's the FBI." It was Hank's voice. Bobby opened the door. "Funny," he said as Hank slipped past him and sat down on the edge of the bed. He glanced at Helen and shook his head in mock distaste. He had a bag of heroin and dumped the powder into a bottle top. "Where'd you get that?" Bobby demanded.

Hank gave the name of a connection. "It's probably garbage." He produced a *bombita*, broke off the glass top, and poured the fluid in with the heroin. Hank held a match under the cooker until the white powder dissolved. Then he put the tip of the needle—the same one Whitey and Helen and the other men had used—into a pea-sized wad of cotton (used to filter out large impurities that might clog the needle) and drew up the liquid from the bottom of the cooker. Borrowing Whitey's belt, he wrapped it around his arm, held the end in his teeth, stuck the needle into a vein, and waited for the blood to start backing up into the eyedropper. Instead of shooting the fluid in immediately he squeezed in a few drops, let it back up into the eyedropper again, squeezed in a little more, let it back up, squeezed more, and continued the in-and-out process until the fluid in the dropper was dark red with blood.

The technique, known as "booting," is believed to prolong the drug's initial effect. He continued booting until there was so much blood in the dropper he was afraid it would coagulate and clog the needle. Then he shot it all in and withdrew the needle. Had the needle clogged, he would have dumped the mixture of blood and drugs back into the cooker, heated it until the blood dissolved, and started over. Addicts call this "shooting gravy": "Because that's what it is—right? Cooked blood?"

Hank put the dropper and needle into a glass of water. "How is it?" one of the men asked. "Garbage," Hank said. "All I feel's the *bombita*."

Whitey had Helen sitting up on the edge of the bed and was brushing her hair again and begging her to stay awake. The phone rang and Bobby talked on it for a minute and then announced he was leaving to sell some of the stolen coffee to a grocer. Around Needle Park it was not uncommon for addicts to steal from one grocer and sell to another, or to steal meat from a supermarket and sell it to a restaurant. "At one point," Bobby explained, "Helen and I were robbing every candy store in the area, mostly for cigarettes. We told one candy-store guy that if he bought all our cigarettes we'd leave him alone. We did quite a business for a while."

Bobby loaded three coffee cases into the elevator, and I rode down with him. He put them out next to the desk in the lobby, and we sat and talked while Bobby waited for someone to pick them up. The hotel had been raided several days earlier—whether because of drugs or prostitution or both, I didn't know—and a uniformed patrolman sat across from us in the lobby next to a two-foot square sign announcing, "This Is a Raided Premises." Evidently the cop and the sign were meant to discourage business. "But the kind of people they get in here," Bobby pointed out, "couldn't care less if it's raided or not. Our whole lives are nothing but one great big raid." Bobby appeared to feel some compassion for the cop. "Look at the poor jerk," he said, "sittin' there, sittin' there, sittin' there, eight hours just sittin' there, nothing to do but stare at all the germs come in here."

The fence walked in then, and Bobby said, ". . . Like him," and then called, "Hey, germ! Over here." An obese man about forty, wth a gray cardigan and brown corduroy pants, pivoted on two tiny feet and exhaled a grunt at Bobby.

"Where's it?" he said, completely without change of expression. Bobby helped him lug the coffee outside, and then asked me if I wanted to come with them. I said no and watched Bobby and the fence leave. Then I took the elevator back upstairs.

Hank let me back in, and the smell and sight were even worse than before. Blood was everywhere—on the carpet, the mattress, the chairs. There was even a five-inch-long finger smear of it on the dressing-table mirror. The room looked as if someone had just been bludgeoned to death in it. Hank and the two other men were still there, sitting around on the floor and in the chairs as if nothing had happened. It was as if the blood were invisible to everyone but me. Suddenly I realized that Helen was not in the room.

"Where's Helen?" I asked.

"Cool it, man," Whitey said. "Don't get all upset. Relax. She's in the bathroom."

I opened the door to the bathroom and found Helen sitting nude on the toilet. She was still half unconscious and was jabbing at her left forearm with a needle and eyedropper. Each time she jabbed, she cried and swore. The words came desperately in a slow, deep, half-conscious mutter. Her arm was covered with jab marks, and blood ran down onto her naked legs.

"Where's the vein?" she cried. "Where's the damned no-good vein, gotta have a vein here, come on, dammit, where are you, vein?" Her head fell forward onto her knees and she sobbed loudly, "Isn't there just one stinking damned vein in my arm that I can get just one stinking damned hit in?"

I was standing in the door and Hank pushed me aside and went in next to Helen. "Here, honey," he said gently, taking her bloody left arm. "Gimme the spike." He lifted the eyedropper and needle from her hand, wiped her arm on his shirt, tightened the tourniquet—one of her own stockings—under her bicep, and tenderly and professionally held the arm to the light. He examined it carefully, squeezed it, rubbed it, tapped it on the main artery, then delicately inserted the needle. Helen had stopped sobbing and watched, absorbed, hoping against hope.

"There," Hank said finally, squeezing the eyedropper. "A good hit. Next time be more careful. You keep blowing shots like that and all you'll have for an arm is abscesses."

The shot took effect immediately. Helen slumped forward, unconscious. I moved toward her, and Hank held out a hand. "Forget it," he said, "she's all right. She'll be around in fifteen minutes jabbing at her arm again. She's been like this before."

We walked back into the bedroom. "All that blood," I said, still stunned. "She must have been jabbing at her arm all over in here."

"That's not from the arm," Whitey said, stretched out on the floor. "She's hemorrhaging. You know, like menstruating, only it ain't because . . ."

"Man, you don't have to explain it to him," Hank broke in, impatient with Whitey's lack of understanding. "He knows what it's about."

I realized then what they meant. Most women addicted to heroin do not menstruate. But Helen had started to bleed anyway, and that was why she had finally ended up in the bathroom.

"She should go to a hospital," I said.

"We keep telling her," Whitey said, "but she don't want to. Anyway she keeps shooting up and passing out. It's that pentobarb or whatever it is"—he held up the bottle—"it really sends you."

I heard a groan. One of the other men who had been in

the room before was lying in a corner on the floor. He groaned again. "What's wrong with him?" I asked.

Hank and Whitey smiled. "He's okay," Whitey said, "he's just a little sick." They smiled again. "Hey, Mickey," Whitey called at him, "how're you doing?" Another groan. Whitey picked up a bottle, similar to the membrane-topped barbiturate bottle Helen had been getting her shots from, and handed it to me. "This is his problem," he said, "but I guess he'll get over it. He boosted a vet's office over on Columbus Avenue and he shot up some of this just 'cause it has that membrane top. You know, he figured it was good stuff, then he finds out it's worming medicine for dogs." He and Hank laughed again, and the man in the corner rolled over and groaned.

Hank and Whitey were themselves stoned on something, probably *bombitas.*

"Look," I said, "Helen really has to get to a hospital." I walked to the phone and picked it up.

Hank leaped over and put his finger on the button. "Wait a minute, man. What are you doing? You can't do that. You call an ambulance and you'll have all kinds of cops all over the place up here. You can't do that, man."

I put the phone down. "All right. I'll call downtown to a hospital and then I'll take her there myself."

"Yeah, man, that's good, that's good, she's gotta go to the hospital, and Whitey and I'll help you, we'll help you."

Whitey jumped up, seized by the urgency of the cause. "Yeah, we'll help you, man, don't worry about nothin', we'll help ya, everything'll be okay, okay."

"Hey!" A loud shout came from the bathroom. "Will

one of you noisy bastards stop running off your mouths out there and get me my damned spike?" And then less loudly, her voice trailing off, "Who stole my damned spike?"

I hurried back into the bathroom. Helen was standing up, her eyes half closed, supporting herself on the sink, rummaging through the medicine cabinet. "Where the hell is my damned spike! Who stole my works?" She started screaming, tears running down her cheeks, a child's wail: "I want my damned spike! I want my damned spike!"

Then she saw me in the door. She moved one supporting hand from the sink to my shoulder, smiled a wide, drunken smile, and leaned against me affectionately. "Hi. You got my damned spike? You know who's got my damned spike?"

"Are you still bleeding?" I asked.

She looked at her arm and rubbed the drying blood, smearing it over her arm. "I think it stopped," she said.

"I don't mean there," I said.

She smiled coyly and leaned against me again. "Oh, that. Yeah, that stopped. I guess I ran out. Left all the blood I had in there." She waved an arm toward the bedroom.

"You've got to go to the hospital, Helen. You've been hemorrhaging and your arm needs treatment and if you keep this up you'll die of an overdose."

"Yeah, I should really go to a hospital. Tomorrow I'll go over to"—she gave the name of a Manhattan hospital— "and see a friend of mine over there . . . who I turned a trick for . . . and he'll get me in."

"You should go tonight, Helen. I'll get you a bed in a hospital downtown."

"Well . . . but . . . you said before none of that, none of that, no help, no conning, none of that, just an ob . . . server."

"Will you go?"

"Call. She'll go," Hank said.

Hank and I got Helen dressed and downstairs to the street. Whitey decided to stay behind and "look after" the man who was sick on dog medicine.

We got a cab on 72nd Street, drove down to the hospital, and finally got Helen admitted. Then we rode back uptown and got out in front of the Martell. When I went to bed it was light out.

Chapter 12

Four hours later someone knocked on my door. I opened it and Bobby stepped into the room, walked angrily over to the window, spun around, walked back to the center of the room, and stood there, feet planted firmly, defiantly.

"Look," he said. "I know you're a square, and that's supposed to make you better than all of us and all that, but what's this with you taking Helen to the hospital? She had a trick last night, you know, and she missed it, and it's not like I'm worried about the bread or anything but he's a very high class guy and if she don't make it, well, he just forgets her and finds another chick. And anyway like I don't go for her just bein' hustled off some place without my knowin' it, you know, like we're very close, Helen and me, and I worry when I can't find her. . . ."

"Look," I interrupted, "Helen was very sick. She had to go to the hospital. It's possible she would be dead now if she hadn't gone . . . And Hank helped me."

Bobby sat down. "Well, you shouldn't have done it without asking me. There I was out there trying to sell those cases of coffee and someone's hustling Helen away some place and keeping her from her trick and now that guy won't call her again and he was one of the last decent tricks she's got."

Bobby sat there, sullen, staring out the window.

"You want to go visit her?" I asked.

"They won't let me in there, she's a junkie. Can you fix it?"

"I can't fix it if it's against the rules. And I guess you're right. It probably is if she's an addict."

"I can tell you it is," Bobby said, grunting.

"Look, I'll see her this afternoon, and I'll tell her I spoke with you and that you miss her, and I'll try to arrange for you to talk to her on the phone. If it's not against the rules. Okay?"

"Sorry I woke you." Bobby got up and went to the door. "See you." The door closed behind him and I went back to bed.

I got up at five that afternoon and went to the hospital. Helen was in a room with another addict, and the two of them were sitting up chatting happily when I walked in.

Helen beamed at me and stuck out her hand. "Hi. They really fixed me up nice here. Of course, I still don't feel too good, but I'm coming fine." Her left arm was in bandages, and without make-up her face looked even more gaunt than usual. She had no eyebrows and her cheeks were sunken.

"Bobby said you'd be here this afternoon. I've been waiting for you." She said it casually, but I could tell she was pleased by my look of surprise.

"Oh, really? I saw him this morning. I thought it was against the rules for him to talk to you."

"Well, I guess it is." She grinned. "But they had visiting hours at ten and he told the nurse downstairs at the desk he was the brother of this patient up the hall."

"How'd he get her name?"

"Well, I told him, of course. What do you think?" I remembered that I had seen a phone booth in the hall when I came in.

I took a close look at her. Her pupils were constricted. "Your eyes are pinned," I said. "You got off."

She grinned again. "Yeah." She would have denied it, except that it gave her pleasure to demonstrate how easily she and Bobby could get around hospital rules. She was volunteering no information, making me dig for each fact, delighted too by the show she was putting on for the other addict.

"How'd you get it? Here? From a nurse?"

"Honey, you should know better than that." She looked at the other girl and laughed. "From a nurse!" They both chuckled. "Honey," Helen said, "if I was gonna get it here

I'd trick one of the doctors, not a nurse. And I can do that, too. There's a young guy was around earlier I'm working on."

"Then you didn't get it here?"

"Nope?" A coy, guess-again smile.

"From Bobby."

She nodded, slowly, still smiling.

"With the works?"

"Right."

"How long ago? When did he leave?"

She leaned her face toward me, looking me straight in the eyes. "Can't you tell? You've been around a while. By now you should be able to look at my eyes and tell me *exactly* how long since I got off."

"How long?" I repeated.

She sat back in the bed. "A couple of hours."

"Twenty minutes," I said.

She sprang up again with glee and clapped her hands together. She looked at the other girl, who was sharing her delight. "He can tell. He can. How about that. Twenty minutes is just about right. In fact, I was afraid you might have run into Bobby down in the lobby. He just left."

"Helen, let's stop playing. How long are you going to stay here? You can stay, you know, till you're detoxified and strong. Three, four, five weeks. How long are you going to stay?"

She became serious. "Honestly, I want to stay just as long as I can. I'm going to stay. I really *want* to clean up. And so does Bobby. We talked about it while he was here. I'm going to stay till I'm strong again and then I can go out and get Bobby off the stuff and make him forget that . . . other thing. . . ." She gave me a knowing look. "You know, that other thing that's gonna end up getting his brains laid out. And then we can both be square."

Chapter 13

I called the hospital that night. Helen had left. "I'm sorry," the nurse said on the phone. "She had a call at the booth here and then she checked herself out."

I hadn't really expected her to stay for weeks—but it was less than two days and she was out already. I went down to the park to look for her and found her sitting with Hank in a luncheonette. She ran over to me and took me to their booth.

"Bobby got busted," she said excitedly, while Hank looked down into his coffee.

"What for?" I asked.

"Discon. For nothing. He was out there in the phone

booth—talking to me—and some lousy bluecoat came along and just busted him for discon, for nothing, for just *being* there."

"Well at least it wasn't a drug bust," I said. "Just discon. What will he get for that?"

"A few days. How much, Hank?"

Hank shrugged. "Less than thirty. Maybe nothing, if he gets a good judge. I mean, the cop didn't have anything on him. It was just 'cause he was a junkie. Like the guy told him to move off the block and when he came back he was still there—in the booth—so he busted him. He might walk."

Helen stood up. "How do you like my outfit?" She was wearing a beige wrap-around skirt and a cloth stole over her shoulder. It looked familiar.

"It's nice. Where'd you get it?"

"At the hospital. I made it. It's a blanket. See?" She unwrapped the skirt enough to show where it had been torn. "Bobby called me just to see how I was, see, and I'm talking to him on the phone and I hear all this commotion and yelling, Bobby yelling, and someone else yelling, it sounded like World War III in the phone booth and then the phone goes dead. So I didn't know what had happened and like I had to get out and help him. You know, I figured he was getting taken off or something and might just be lying out here some place, and none of these creeps around here would do anything for him, not even look for him if they didn't see him around awhile, so I ripped up one of the city's very best blankets and with the pajama top I made

myself quite an outfit—don't you think?—and grabbed a
subway uptown and found Hank and he told me what happened."

"When will we know what his sentence is?" I asked.

"I'll find out tomorrow," Hank said. "I'll call the court
clerk or something. Now I gotta go work. There's a nice
little apartment I know."

Helen and I said goodbye to Hank and walked over to
the Reynolds Hotel, where Helen knew a friend with a
room.

"He might be able to score," she said as we crossed the
street. "He knows some people uptown I don't know that
he might be able to cop from. I don't want you to think I
didn't mean what I said in the hospital about getting clean,
but I just need something now to get me straight so I can
get some more clothes and find out about Bobby. When I
find out what's happening to him I'll go back in. If I can get
back in."

We went up to a small room on the sixth floor and
Mickey, the junkie who had shot up the worming medicine,
let us in. "Glad to see you've recovered," I said.

"Yeah, man, that was a pretty lousy high. Next time, I
read labels—I can tell you that."

"Listen, baby," Helen started when the door was closed.
"Can you cop for me uptown? I really gotta get straight,
man, and I'm sick, I'm really sick."

I looked at her. In the luncheonette she had been as un-
sick as I was, but now, conning Mickey, her eyes were tear-
ing and she was rubbing her nose.

"Come on, baby, just this once, just for me," Helen pleaded.

"Helen, I can't cop up there, like there's a real panic, you know that, I can't score anywhere in this whole city, and I been trying all day."

Helen's whole personality changed. The childish, wheedling attack was abandoned. Now she was angry. "Look, you bastard, you haven't scored all day but you're straight." She grabbed his arm and turned him toward the mirror. "Look at those eyes. Pinpoints. You're straight as my Aunt Minnie, buddy, don't give me that crap. If you had anything in you at all besides junk you'd go up there and cop for me."

It wasn't working. Mickey was unmoved. She slipped from anger into understanding. "Okay, Mickey, I'm sorry, I know you'd cop for me if you could. It's just that I'm so sick, or I wouldn't even be going on like this. Forget it. Please. I'm really sorry."

"Oh, come on, Helen, I'm sorry. I know how it is to be sick. You've seen me lots of times when I was sicker than you are now, but I mean if I can't score I can't score, that's all there is to it. I'm sorry, kid, but what can I tell you? There just isn't any stuff around."

"I know you'd score for me if you could, Mickey." She put an arm around his shoulder, and turned to me. "Mickey and I used to go together, when Bobby was on the rock, didn't we, Mickey?" Mickey looked embarrassed and she kissed him on the cheek and put both arms around his waist. She moved easily from emotion to emotion, searching for one that would turn the key.

"I really liked those times, Mickey. I mean of course I was sorry Bobby was locked up, but it was nice, wasn't it? And I remember then you used to score for me, so I know you would now too if you could. Bobby got busted a little while ago, did you know that? I think for felonious possession. I'll need someone to work with out here. I've got lots of good tricks and I need someone to work with me, take care of me, someone I can depend on to be able to cop for me when I need it. . . ."

Mickey pulled her hands back from around his waist. "Which is always, right Helen? You need it always. I don't need no girls to support *my* habit, Helen, I manage all right."

Now tears. Hysteria. Torrents of tears. She put her head on my shoulder and really let go. Between the sobs: "Mickey, don't do this to me, don't do this, Mickey, I'll do anything for you, turn tricks for you, boost for you, anything, Mickey, anything, but I got to have something, I got to, please score for me, Mickey, I know you can, you're going to have to score for yourself soon anyway, you can score just one extra trey for me, just one, Mickey, just to take the edges off, Mickey, please, please, I'm begging you, Mickey."

Her sobs had grown to wails and she lifted her head from my shoulder to show Mickey that the tears were real. She caught my eye then, and through her tears, she winked.

"Oh, dammit, Helen," Mickey said, "shut up, will you? Shut up before they throw me out of here, will you? All right. All right. When I go up to score, I'll try to get you something. But I'm not promising. If I can, I will. That's all.

If I can, I will. But treys are $7 now. You got the bread?"

"Of course I've got it. Would I be going through all this if I didn't?"

She turned to me. "Can you let me have seven bucks? I'll give it back tonight after I get straight and go out and work a little."

It dawned on me then that the con I had been admiring for the past few minutes had been on me as well as Mickey. Now that Mickey—who had so resolutely resisted right up to the final act—had succumbed, how could a square resist without showing himself even more heartless than a heartless junkie? I gave her seven dollars. She handed the money over to Mickey, who promised to come back in an hour. Helen and I sat down to wait.

After an hour and a half Helen started getting nervous. In two hours she was hanging out the window, looking up the block for Mickey, pretty sure now that he had beat her for the seven dollars. Who had conned whom? She gave him another fifteen minutes and then started ransacking the room for whatever she could find. She went through the bureau drawers and the medicine chest, both empty. She searched under the edges of the carpet, on top of the wardrobe, behind the radiator, behind the bureau. Finally, stuck under the sink, she found a set of works—eyedropper, needle, bottle top—wrapped in brown paper with a rubber band.

"Well, it wasn't a total loss, anyway," she said. "Now all I need is something to shoot up." She looked at me, and I shook my head. "Okay, okay," she said. "I won't ask.

Wait here for me, will you? And if that bastard Mickey just happens to come back, hold him for me." She rushed out. I waited, and wondered how long it would be before she came back, if she ever did. She was back in thirty minutes, out of breath. Without speaking, she bolted the door and dumped a tiny pill the size of a saccharin tablet into the bottle top with some water. She cleaned the needle in a paper cup full of water and then put the large end in her mouth and blew air through it.

"I hate shooting someone else's corroded blood," she said. The pill was Dilaudid, a synthetic opiate. She gave herself the shot and sat down on the bed.

"That Dilaudid is somethin' else," she said, starting to nod. "Just one of the little things and I'm straight."

"Where'd you get it?"

"From this croaker up on 76th Street. He used to write for me, you know, scripts, prescriptions. I turned a trick with him. I hadn't seen him in a long time . . . and I guess . . ." She was nodding.

"Yes?" I said.

She brought her head back up, like a dozing driver who sees headlights coming. "I guess he was hot for me 'cause he hadn't seen me in so long . . . so he . . . gave me a Dilaudid . . . I told him I was up real tight . . . which is the truth for sure . . . for sure. . . ." She was sitting on the edge of the bed, and as she nodded she leaned backward, searching for the wall to lean against. Finally she went all the way back, touching the wall with the back of her neck. In that position she took a pack of cigarettes from her purse.

"How do you feel?" I asked.

"Relaxed . . . warm . . . secure. . . ." She paused fifteen or twenty seconds between each word. After four or five minutes she remembered about the cigarettes and drew one from the pack, but forgot about it before she got it to her mouth. She was absorbed in something far more important than a cigarette.

"I haven't been so high in *so* long. This is somethin', this Dilaudid." She put the cigarette in her mouth finally and lighted it. I asked again how she felt.

"Warm . . . nice . . ." She stopped, slouched back, and closed her eyes completely.

"Can you hear me? Are you asleep?"

She answered immediately, clearly, wide awake. "No, honey, I'm not asleep . . . I'm takin' a trip . . ." Her eyes closed again.

"Why do you use stuff?" I asked.

"Why do I use junk? Ask me something hard. Why do you think I use it?" She was holding the cigarette between her fingers and kept letting her hand drop onto the bed. Each time the lighted end touched the bed, she pulled it back up.

"I don't know."

"That's a good answer." She fell sideways onto the bed, crushing the cigarette under her. "Fall on your face, Helen," she said to herself, then sat back up straight and tried the cigarette. It was out and she threw it on the floor. She scratched her nose. "Shows how clean I am from this panic. My nose is itching." She took a brush from her purse and started brushing her hair. She was coming out of the nod a little.

"Why do I use drugs? Well, I'll tell you. I started at home, in Denver, when I was nineteen. With chlorohydrate. No. I didn't use it. I mean I didn't take it. I used it for knockout drops. It comes in crystals and you just put a few drops in somebody's drink and they get very sleepy. They think they're getting drunk."

"What was the purpose of doing that?"

"To rob them."

"Were you working as a prostitute then?"

"Yes. Because a man told me that I would make very, very good money, that I was a lovely girl, and that I could start out as a $100 call girl any time I wanted. And I didn't believe him. And he showed me a couple of $100 Johns and I made them. Consequently, I made a couple of hundred dollars. I did that for maybe five months and then I came to New York on vacation, and I went to this club down in the Village. It was one of the female-impersonator clubs, filled with queers, all the performers were queer, and it turned out that the men waiting on tables were really girls dressed as men. And so I started going out with one of the waiters and we made it together and I spent the rest of my vacation with her and then I went back to Denver. And when I got back there she used to write to me a lot and then she came out there and I saw her and she brought me back to New York. And I lived with her for awhile and worked in this same club she did. And that's how I met Bobby. When I worked at this club, I stopped going with

this girl and started going with someone else for awhile . . ."
She started to nod again.

"Helen, you're nodding. You were going to tell me how you met Bobby."

"I am *not* nodding," she almost shouted. "I was *going* to tell you that I went with someone else at the club, a guy. We'd gone out for a while and then I met Bob's brother Hank, who says he fell in love with me, which is a bunch of boloney 'cause he fell in love with anything in skirts that would pay any attention to him. Then Bobby came over to the house one time, and Hank said, 'Helen, you don't mind if my kid brother Bobby takes off in the bathroom, do you?' And I said, 'I most certainly do.' Because I wasn't using drugs then. I said, 'There's gonna be no junk in this house.' He said, 'Well, he's going to do it anyway.' So I said, 'All right. This once, but never again.' And this went on for about three days. And I grabbed hold of Bobby and told him, I said, 'Why are you doing this? Why are you trying to kill yourself? It's ridiculous.' I probably gave him the same lecture that anybody else gives any other junkie, and that I've had myself many a time. So that particular night I talked him out of taking off. At least he didn't take off inside my house. He probably went and took off in the nearest restaurant or gas station, I don't know. But he was on parole and he had to be home at twelve o'clock. One thing led to another and Bobby and I became very fond of each other. Bobby started staying overnight at my house against his PO's wishes and his mother's wishes. I guess we just started going together then. And then one day I had a bad toothache. I couldn't get a doctor. So Bobby gave me a very weak shot." She nodded.

"Go ahead. You're nodding again."

"Well, I don't even know where I was now."

"You were telling me about the toothache."

"And you're telling me I'm nodding and I'm not."

"Well, if you're not nodding, just go ahead."

"For the toothache Bobby gave me a shot, and it took the toothache away, and it also took my fear of drugs away. So I started doing it myself. Bobby'd be in the bedroom sleeping and I'd be taking off. I took off the first time by myself. No one prompted me. In fact, I was scared to death of Bobby catching me. And I had a habit before I knew it. One morning we both woke up sick. I'd had a habit for quite some time before he knew it. We were living right in the same house and he didn't know I was using. I was buying it for him, scoring for him. 'Cause I said I didn't have any record and on the first offense I'd get a suspended sentence. So I copped for him and kept some for myself. I was getting the money hooking. A hundred dollars a date, maybe $2,200 a week. And Bobby was doing nothing. Sitting home, doing nothing. Shooting up, sleeping, watching TV, reading, having his buddies over, turning them on. He had a real ball.

"After the first shot for the toothache, I was curious. Curiosity's why you first start. But I dug it, you know? I dug the relaxed feeling. So I kept going. It makes me very relaxed. Completely relaxed and not nervous about anything. Nothing fazes you. You could hear about your mother dying an excruciating death and you wouldn't even shed a tear. You know, you'd feel bad about it, but your emotions are, you know, to a great extent subdued. And that lasts about four hours, maybe longer.

"But it's murder, what you go through, what you have to go through every day. Every day. And every day is different. There is absolutely no routine in this life. The only routine is that you need that shot when you wake up. When you get up, you take off. This is generally around twelve or one o'clock when you get up anyway, in the afternoon. I generally, if I'm not goofing, I get on the phone and make some calls and arrange to have some dates for the evening. And I'll go out and score if I can. If I don't have any money, I'll make it my business to have an afternoon date so I'll have enough money to go out and score. While I'm straight I can do this. And Bobby does nothing. Usually he lays in bed and nods."

"Have you ever been sorry that you went on the stuff three years ago?"

"I imagine that I've been sorry every day that I've had a habit."

"Why don't you kick?"

"That's just about what I did now. I was forced to. With this panic there hasn't been any junk on the streets. There *is* junk around but you can't get it. The average junkie can't get it. He has to know somebody pretty good. Doors are shut tighter than a drum. And people that are out selling anything are selling baking soda, and not heroin. You get home and it won't even cook up. And they're charging you

$10 for it. So it's no good. I'd rather kick and get clean and be square. That's probably what will happen eventually. I would have done it before but Bobby didn't want to do it. But I might do it now. I just might do it. I don't want to start right into a job. I want to go on a vacation first somewhere . . . anywhere. I want to go to Puerto Rico.

"I can't stand these other junkies. They're pigs. Actually, when I look at them I'm probably seeing myself in a mirror and I can't stand it. They're animals . . . we're all animals. We'll step on one another for a shot if there's no junk. I've seen it. I never knew what a panic was, before this one. I wasn't around before to see what a panic does to people. There's no junk to be found, and then when it's there, people claw each other, and stomp each other to get to it. Bobby told me that once in a panic he paid $30 for a nickel bag. But if worse gets to worse, I get Dilaudid. I can con a doctor out of Dilaudid. And I don't mean just by tricking the guy like I did this time, 'cause he's something different. Once I told this doctor I had kidney stones and got him to write for me, but all he wrote for was four Dilaudids. But he gave me two Tuinals in his office and when he went to get the water for them I stole some prescription blanks off his desk. And I passed all kinds of phony scripts. I still have the original. Maybe you can help me cash it. It's an original script. No, I guess you wouldn't. No one would. I really don't have any friends like that. You can't have junkie friends, I mean ones you can trust. Because they're junkies. I can't even trust Bobby. I had my wake-up three days ago right here on the table next to me. When I got up it was gone, and Bobby was the only one that was straight that morning. Everyone was sick but Bobby. And I *know* Bobby didn't have a wake-up.

"But like I said, I could—and I have—con a doctor out of Dilaudids. I dress as well as I can. I say, 'Doctor, I have a kidney stone, and I've got to go to the hospital. I can't go right now, because I have two small children at home and my husband pulled the ligaments in his foot and I've got to be there to take care of him. My doctor just recently passed away. That's the reason I'm here. I went to his office for the medication that he had been giving me right along, and his nurse wrote down what I had had. Here it is.' And I show him a piece of paper with it written down —Dilaudid number 30 so on and so forth. And any doctor who wasn't suspicious would write out a script for twenty or thirty Dilaudids. Possibly one, definitely two would get me straight. But that's no good either. I mean a Dilaudid habit is no good. First of all, your habit on Dilaudid, you get it much faster than you do on stuff. Your body tolerances build up fast and before you know it you're taking fifteen or twenty Dilaudids at once, where maybe three days before, one or two would help. It goes up fantastically high. Second, there isn't a doctor in New York that isn't hip to junkies. But I'll tell you that if a doctor can be conned by anyone, I can do it. I can con anyone.

"Anybody I want to do something for me, I can make them do it. Just by talking. I've always been able to do this, since I was a little girl, since I first told a lie to my father. My father was too strict. I had to think up reasons to get out of the house to do the things I wanted to do. So that's what I did. I started on my father. It worked on him. It worked on my mother. It worked on teachers, and it worked on everybody else. The only thing you really need is a sincere approach. If someone thinks you're sincere they'll do anything in the world for you. I can cry, too, any time I want. Like you saw me do just now with Mickey. I don't even remember the first time I did it. When I was a kid, if ever I was going to get a licking—not a licking but a punishment rather—that I didn't want, I used to cry and say, 'Gee, I'm sorry.' My parents felt so bad about my feeling sorry that they wouldn't do anything. Even now there's one policeman who calls me the actress. This is a cop who doesn't believe anybody. You can tell him the truth and he won't believe you, and you can tell him a lie and he won't believe you. No matter what you tell him, he won't believe you. So he calls me the actress 'cause he says I'm the only one that really sounds sincerely sorry and up-set and so on and so forth. It works on him, even though he knows I'm acting. I like the man. I sincerely like him.

"So like I said I can con just about anyone. In the hos-pital, for example, I told you I was working on one of the doctors. I wasn't kidding. But I didn't want to take off on junk. I asked Bobby to bring me out some pot. Either pot or bring me out a pill or something. But he brought me junk, so I used it. I felt like getting high like any other human being would do. How many fellas cash their pay checks on Friday night and go out and have a good time? I wanted to get high. I was bored. I felt so *normal*. But I went into the hospital with the idea of kicking and staying clean. I really wanted to. I didn't want anything more to do with drugs or anything like that. But, as it worked out, Bobby got busted and I came out. And I started right back. I had to come out because Bobby needed me. He always needs me. I think that's the extent though. I don't think he loves me. I don't think I mean that much to Bobby any more. Bobby's just afraid of losing a meal ticket.

"I've taken care of Bobby since I've known him. He hasn't had to work. He hasn't had to do anything. For me, you might say he's just another arm to feed. I have to do all the work, and I have to do some pretty lousy things, hustling and conning and stealing and all that. But, well, I wouldn't go around mugging people like people think junkies do. There may be a couple of guys that are stupid enough—not stupid, they have to be mentally ill—to go around hitting people over the head for their money. If I'm real, real sick, I usually go out and grab myself a trick, just like I did now, which isn't hard to do. Junk has made me smarter. It's made me more cunning than I was before. Because I have to be cunning, like an animal, because I live like an animal. Like now I'm turning $15 tricks when I used to turn hundred's. I'm going with men that I wouldn't look at before.

"And I push. Everybody does. Every junkie at some time or another deals stuff. Actually, I've only done it two or three times. Once a large connection asked me if I wanted to work for him, that's all. I said, 'All right,' the percentage was right, so he gave me a bundle on consignment. And I sold it, and then turned the money back. He gave me another one or maybe two. Then I turned that stuff over. That's all there was to it. Then I got afraid of being busted and I stopped. Another time I stopped because the guy didn't show up again, and I found out why, because he was out of business himself. His partner had taken off with his stash. So that's the way it is. Everybody pushes. Like right now Bobby is the biggest dealer on the street out there, I mean in Needle Park. He's got all of Little Tony's old pushers working for him and he's even getting stuff from one of Little Tony's cutters. Now how he's doing that I couldn't tell you, but there's got to be something wrong about it. Got to be. Little Tony just isn't that kind of guy, to stand still for something like that. Bobby's crazy to be doing what he's doing. One of Little Tony's men is going to step into him one of these days and then that'll be that."

"What was your reaction the first time you took junk?"

"I was very relaxed, very high, I grooved with it. I liked it. I didn't get sick. Most people get violently sick to their stomachs the first time. I didn't. Possibly if I had I wouldn't be a junkie today. Some kind of people can become junkies and others can't. For example, a strong-willed person will not become a junkie. It takes someone who's extremely sensitive, or who is weak-willed. I don't think I'm weak-willed, but I'm very sensitive. Bobby is both, although he tries to make everybody think he's King Kong. He's not. So here I am, a real junkie. I guess you might say a real bad one. Like the worst habit I ever had was $135 a day. And

I kicked that one cold-turkey 'cause I didn't know what I was in for. If I had known what I was in for I never would have done it. It isn't so much the physical pain as it is nerves. It's nerves. But the time I kicked that really bad habit I fell out of bed three or four times. You know, I just rolled right off the bed. I vomited. I felt like somebody just kept punching me in the stomach. My nerves and vomiting are the two things. I've never had too much trouble with backaches and stuff like that.

"This time I haven't gotten sick at all. Of course, now I had a shot. It puts me right back on the bandwagon. I'd gone through two days of withdrawal, on GB's and in the hospital. Bobby said if I could go until tomorrow night I'd be through it. But I took a shot, because I couldn't stand it, which means that I have the whole thing to go through again. I don't understand why. All it's doing now is it's relaxed my body. So I have the whole thing to go through again. But I will. I have to. Because I want to kick. I hate this life. I can't stand it. Can't stand the way I live. I don't live from day to day or pay check to pay check. I live from fix to fix. I think of myself first, whereas at one time everything I had I split right down the middle with Bobby. Now I don't do that any more. I'll take my fix first, and if I just happen to catch somebody with money I'll go out and score again for him. Living like this is like living in a . . . I don't know, you don't take pride in where you live, or your appearance, or anything. If you do get dressed it's for a reason, it's because you're going out to make some money. It has nothing to do with actual self-pride. Very

few junkies have any self-pride. They may tell you they
do, but they're full of baloney. The only pride they take
is in that fix every four hours. And if they happen to cop
a better bag than somebody else, this is the grooviest thing
they can do. Like I say, they're animals.

"There are very few male junkies who do anything but
live off girls. Most of the girls have to go out and hustle
and if they don't bring back the money the guy makes all
kinds of trouble for her. The other morning, sick as I was,
Bobby insisted that I go with this John and Bobby brought
him up to me. Now Bobby's been dealing, so he should
have all kinds of bread. But he tells me he got taken off,
that he's broke. So I turned the trick. I never saw any junk
for it, and I gave the money to Bobby. That's why I say
junkies are animals, and I'm just as much an animal as anybody else because I'll fight anybody for a bag if I haven't
got it. That's something I wouldn't do before. I wouldn't
fight. And I don't even have a home, a place to stay. I just
stay where I can. This one's house, that one's house. Or
I'll stay up and walk the streets all night, all day, until some
cafeteria opens. Then I'll sit down and have some coffee.
And Bobby sticks with me, hoping that I'll get a room.
Except once I stayed with him in that fourth-floor bathroom in the Martell. I stayed over a couple nights. But I'm
afraid in there, though. I got caught in there once. Bobby
got off and left me holding the bag, so to speak. And I had
the manager on my heels, for at least two blocks. I ran like
hell, but Bobby was out first. And being a girl, I suppose
they figured they'd collar me. So they chased me, figuring

I had stuff on me, which I did, but I got away. I don't get tossed too often. One time I got tossed three days in a row. Usually I don't. Maybe once every two months. But they never find anything on me. Not because I'm clean. I'm never clean. I've almost always got works or pills or something. But they can't look where I carry the things. And when they're tossing me I start crying and screaming and making a scene and they get nervous. It's very effective. I yell, 'You're always picking on me. Why don't you leave me alone? I haven't done anything. I'm clean. I don't even use junk any more. You people are driving me right back to it.' And so on and so forth. You know, and then they kind of leave you alone. That's when they stop searching me. But if they do get something on you, you can't try that act in court. Because it won't work on a judge, I'll tell you. Judges get aggravated by scenes and crying. They like to get one case after the other finished. The judge doesn't want all that nonsense."

"What do you think is going to become of you eventually, Helen?"

"I don't know. I'll probably die early. It won't be from junk, but it'll be from the causes of junk or a liver ailment or hepatitis or something. I don't care any more. I really don't. 'Cause there's nothing for me. So it'll be something from junk. Everything's so filthy. I don't even have a pot to boil anything. And when there're six junkies getting off on one spike, you don't have time to boil anything anyway. I saw somebody shoot my blood the other day because there was some *bombita* in it. Now this is something. This guy is not a bona-fide junkie, so to speak, just chipping. And like *we* don't even do that. Bobby did it once when I had hepatitis. He tried to get it so he could go into Metropolitan Hospital with me. But he didn't.

"I'll tell you, I don't really think there's any answer to this whole thing, this junk thing. I think the answer's just to stay away from it. If all the psychiatrists in Kentucky and so forth can't figure it out, how the hell can I? I just use the stuff. I dig junk, I won't kid anybody. And I don't have any *reason* to quit. Nothing means anything to me. I don't give a good damn about anything."

"Do you ever look at a square girl on the street . . ."

"And envy her? Yes. Every day. Because she doesn't *know* what I know. I could *never* be a square like that. I was once, but once I took that first shot, that shattered the whole bit, because then I *knew*. I knew what it was to be high. I knew what it was to groove with junk. Even the first habit that I kicked, which was the worst that I ever kicked, I kicked cold on my own volition. I still went back to junk. Right in this very hotel. I bought my first fix here. I found some excuse or other to do it. I'll tell you right now. I wouldn't care if I died. I just hope it isn't painful, that's all. Because I'll never be like that girl on the street. Never, never. I *can't* be just like she is . . . can't be. Because she doesn't know what I know. She hasn't gone through what I've gone through. Her mind isn't going to constantly revert back to 'Maybe I'll just take one shot because it's Saturday night, what the hell.' No.

"I take stuff because I dig the high, that's all. I like the feeling, I like the feeling of *not* feeling. What is it the Spanish say? *No siento nada?* I feel nothing. That's just the way you get to feel—nothing. *Nothing* fazes you. But then it wears off and you've got to cop again. And when you cop, you don't know whether you're going to get caught with that bag on you or whether you're going to get it home.

"Let me tell you something, what goes on in your mind. All right, let's say it costs me $10 a fix. It costs me a hell of a lot more than that now, but let's say it costs me $10 a fix. Okay. Well. I have my $10. Now what I have to do is go out and look for a connection, unless I have a house connection or think of someone that lives somewhere who has good junk, which is very rare. Last night I went up to 112th, 111th Street. I went uptown where the better junk is. Okay. I have my $10. I want to get two $5 bags, which of course during this panic you're paying . . . for a $5 bag you're paying $10 and $15, for a $3 bag you're paying $5 and up. Okay. So I go and ask someone, 'Who's got the best stuff around here?' 'Chico has.' Okay. Chico has. Someone else says Armando has. Then I have to find out who's who and who has the better stuff, Armando or Chico. Meanwhile, you're walking on this street, and you know darn well the narcos are watching you. You *know* it. You *feel* it. But you don't care because you're sick. So you're going to take that chance anyway. Now, you don't want to jeopardize the connection, either. So all right you're gonna cop off Chico. You walk by Chico and say, 'I want two,' and keep walking. Then you turn around and you come back and you give him the money and at the same time you say you want two. Then you come back and he gives you the two.

"Now if Chico decides to beat you, Chico's just gonna turn around and walk away. And you're dead. Your $10 are gone with the wind. Or maybe you're going to get it home and find out it's baking soda. The fellow you met steered you wrong because he's getting a piece of it. This doesn't often happen when it's not panic time. On just ordinary days everybody's got stuff, some better than others. Then after you cop, most of the time you have to walk home because you don't have that much money for a cab. Buses take too long and you're standing on that corner with stuff on you. So all the time you're walking, you're praying, you're saying to yourself now, 'Is there a narco around that knows my face and is going to call me over just for the hell of it?' Which they do. Meanwhile, you've got stuff on you, and you're sick. You never know, you're never relaxed until you feel the stuff in you, and then you know that within four hours you've got to get some money, and the stuff again. This is gonna go on. And you know that before you go to bed at night, you not only have to have your bedtime fix, but you have to have your wake-up. So that's $20 right there that you *must* have . . . you absolutely *must* have. And you have to cop before you go to bed because when you wake up you might be too sick to be able to go out and cop.

"And now with this panic it's almost impossible to cop anyway. Even up in Harlem it's hard to cop. I went up there last week, I walked up there with a knife open. That's the way you have to walk up there. They see a white in Harlem and they're ready to jump all over you. So you walk out there with a knife—or like Hank did the other day. He carries a .45 right out in the open. I've never really used a knife, but I could, and I know how. And I'm capable. And I'll cut anybody who threatens me. That's what I mean about being an animal. Two years ago, three years ago, I couldn't have hurt a fly. But when you don't care about your own life—that much—then you know what you care about someone else's life. And when someone threatens the little bit of care that you *do* have for your own life, then you know what you're going to do to them. I could kill somebody and it wouldn't faze me if they're gonna hurt me. Just like Hank said he ripped somebody's stomach wide open and when he found out his guts weren't falling out he put his hand in and pulled them out. He made *sure* that guy died. And I could do the same damned thing. I haven't just because I haven't had any opportunity, I haven't had any reason. I haven't caught anybody at the particular time. But Bobby has. I saw Bobby stab a guy twelve times. Because he beat Bobby for $500. And he's cut me too. He went off. He went crazy behind *bombitas*. He didn't cut me bad. I broke the blade of the knife off. Bobby's not that strong. I mean, he's strong, but I'm strong too.

"This is like a jungle, and you know damn well you have to protect yourself. If you're going to stand there and let people, you know, go all over you, then you're pretty stupid. Because you're just asking to be hurt. Like I said, they're animals. And I'm no different than any other one. I'll beat somebody as soon as look at them. I'll beat somebody for their money just as fast as look at them now. I'm just as treacherous and nasty as the rest. I found this out during this panic. I didn't know it before. I didn't know myself before. For example, I never beat anybody for their money before, especially a sick addict. But last week when I was sick myself, a girl came up to me and she had $30. I had just been beat for my money. She had $30. She said, 'Helen, can you cop?' I said, 'Yes.' I took the money and I never came back. And I didn't intend to come back from the very beginning. She waited, oh, I'd say she waited about ten hours. That's a long time to wait. And then she left and she never came back. How could she come back? She was still sick. And besides, I wasn't afraid of her."

"What's the very first thing you remember in your whole life, Helen?"

"I remember when I was a kid walking into a party with all my clothes off and everybody thought it was cute. I was just a cute little girl. I *was* a cute little girl—until they started telling me what to do and my father started to be a tyrant. My father started to use military tactics on me. He never hit me. But he messed my mind up. He made me sit on a straight-backed chair for three or four hours at a time with my hands folded, without talking . . . three years old . . . made me stand at attention three and four hours till my back felt like it was breaking. That's all. But I never cried, not to my father. Or to my mother. My mother was an angel. But I cried to my aunts and uncles. I got what I wanted."

She had stopped nodding. She was straight now—no runny nose, no watery eyes. She appeared perfectly normal except for the constricted pupils.

"What are you going to do now?" I asked.

"What do I always do? Go out and try to hustle the next fix. If I can find that bastard Mickey. . . ."

book three

Chapter 14

I awoke the next day at one in the afternoon, showered, dressed, and went hunting for Hank or Helen to ask about Bobby. Neither one was on the benches or in the coffee shop, so I went over to the Reynolds and tried Mickey's room. Helen was still there. She had not gone out to look for Mickey and had been sleeping since I left.

"You hear anything about Bobby?" she asked.

"No. That's why I was looking for you." She got up and wrapped the needle, eyedropper, and bottle top in the brown paper she had found it in. "Can't leave this stuff around like this," she said. "Here I was sleeping all night with it out just like that. I'm lucky The Man didn't come crashing in here and bust me."

Someone knocked on the door. "Who is it?" Helen called.

"Hotchner." The voice sounded impatient.

"See what I mean?" Helen whispered, stuffing the works into her bra. "The narcos." She opened the door. Hotchner was alone. He was about twenty-four, tall, slender, tightly built, with bright red hair cascading over his forehead. He wore a gray cord jacket with striped tie and button-down shirt. He looked more like a college student than a cop.

"Where's your partner?" Helen asked, very friendly.

"Sick. Not working today." He looked at me.

"This is a friend of mine," she said, then seeing the look on Hotchner's face, laughed and added, "No, baby, not *that* kind of friend. He's a writer. He's writing about junkies."

Hotchner warmed up a little and put out his hand. "You've got a good guide if you want to see the junk world," he said. "Helen can show it all to you." Helen and Hotchner seemed very close, like old friends.

"Look," Hotchner said to Helen, "I gotta talk to you. How about . . ." He caught himself.

"That's okay," Helen said. "It's all right. Go ahead."

"How about Central Park, same place, just inside, right away. I'll wait. So hurry, will you, Helen?"

"Will I hurry? Look, man, I'm not sniffing like this 'cause I've got a cold, you know. Boy, could I have used you last night." Hotchner left and she closed the door.

She sat down on the bed. "He won't be there for thirty minutes. He says right away, the bastard, and he won't be there for thirty minutes." Her friendliness toward Hotchner had vanished. "So I'll just wait thirty minutes and then a few more and make *him* sit around out there."

"What does he want?" I asked.

"What do you think he wants? What does any man want? He wants me to turn a trick, that's what he wants."

"With him?"

"Right, baby," she said sarcastically, "with him. How do you think I stay on the street? How do you think I keep from getting busted every two minutes, the way these other junkies do?"

"Well, while you wait for your thirty minutes, I think I'll go see if I can find Hank and see if he knows anything about Bobby."

I walked up to 72nd Street and then across to Central Park. I looked around on the benches under the arbor leading into the park from the street and found Hotchner.

"What's wrong," the detective said, "she not coming or something?"

"She's coming. But she won't be here for a minute. I came because I'm curious."

"Yeah? About what?"

"She told me why she's meeting you here, but I'm not sure I believe her."

Hotchner grinned. "Well, I don't know what she told you but I can just give you a good rule of thumb with her and with any junkie. If she told it to you, it's almost got to be a lie. What did she tell you? No. I can guess.

Because she would never tell you why she's really coming here, so what she probably told you was she's tricking me."

"That's right."

"Look, are you really writing about junkies? Is that on the level?"

"Yes."

"Okay, you want to know about junk, right? Well, Helen can show you a lot. With her you'll probably see things even I wouldn't ever see. But there's other things too. Like for example why she's meeting me here today. Look, if you want to, go wait for me awhile till I finish with her and we can talk. If you want to. Okay?"

"Where?"

"In the Automat. Second floor. At 72nd Street and Amsterdam Avenue, right up the street here. You know where it is?"

It was the same place I had first met Bobby. "Yes. I know it. I'll wait."

Chapter 15

We sat at a table in the back on the second floor where it was quiet. Hotchner talked. He seemed very earnest and very eager to have people understand the drug world.

"One thing a junkie will never—never—tell you is when they rat," Hotchner said. "They might tell you everything else and let you see everything and all that, but they won't admit to you when they rat. Because that's the worst, the absolutely worst thing that anyone in that world can do. I mean, if someone beats them for some money, they'll forget it. They'll even forget it if you deal them a dummy. But rat. No, sir. That is something else. That is the worst.

"You see, a junkie gets busted, right? Okay, he knows

there's a good chance that he'll beat the thing in court and walk out. If he doesn't beat it, if the cop's really got him right, then he has two alternatives. One is to take an Article Nine—that means accept commitment to a hospital. If he does that he avoids trial and sentencing and just goes to a hospital for about three months and then after he gets out he has to keep seeing a follow-up authority, like a probation officer, for about nine more months. That's if the charge is a misdemeanor, like say possession. If it's a felony, like selling, he's got to keep going in the program for three years. Well, usually if it's a misdemeanor the guy's not going to take it. He figures why should he do three months in a hospital and then have to stay clean on the street for another nine months when he can plead guilty, get a six-month sentence, serve four—he gets two off for good behavior—and then be back out on the street to do as he pleases. So he turns down the hospital option.

"Now the second alternative he likes a lot better. Because with this one he does no time at all. He agrees to work for the narco who busted him—to be a stool. The narco tells the DA this guy wants to work and the DA gets the case put off a couple of weeks and the cop puts up the junkie's bail. Then the junkie sets up a few connections for the narco, he makes the arrests, tells the DA, who tells the judge, and the judge gives the junkie a suspended sentence.

"And a lot of these junkies don't cut loose from the narco then, either. They want to *keep* working for you. It does something for their egos or something. And they figure they build up a little insurance with the narco, you know, so when they get busted again their cooperation gives them an edge with the court, or maybe the narco can get them cut loose before they're booked.

"So now we get to Helen. Right now there's one helluva panic, I guess you know that. Well, Helen has been ratting on just about every connection on the West Side. Not to get a light sentence for anything, but to get the junk. She sets the guy up, my partner and I bust him, keep most of the stuff for evidence, and give her a couple of bags. You couldn't work something like that if there weren't a panic. But with this panic she'll do anything to get stuff."

"If she knows these connections," I said, "why doesn't she just score off them? Instead of ratting on them to you?"

"Because for one thing their stuff is too expensive. I mean, really good stuff now is going for maybe $20, $30 for a nickel bag. And also because sometimes these guys won't deal to her. They've got their own regular customers and there isn't that much, that they can deal to everyone. So she figured out a way to get the stuff without paying for it. She's a clever girl. Just now over in Central Park there she gave me another guy up in Harlem she says has good stuff. She'll go up there and finger the guy for us when he has the stuff on him, and we'll bust him. It's against department regulations, of course, giving her any of the stuff, but so what? It gets pushers locked up, and that's all I care about. I'll tell you, when I came into the bureau a year ago I figured I was really going to stamp out narcotics. After a few months I got afraid narcotics were going to stamp me out. Anything I can do to lock up a pusher, I'm gonna do it.

"People don't understand. They don't know what it

takes to get a pusher locked up. We get letters every day
from people giving us the names and nicknames and de-
scriptions and addresses of pushers, and you can tell that
the people who write those letters think all we've got to
do is just go over there and pick the guy up. But it's not
that way. I'll bet that right now I know more pushers who
are working than a lot of junkies do. But just picking up
a pusher and getting him into court is not getting him into
jail. For example, someone comes up to you in the street
and hits you in the mouth. Okay, you call a cop, he takes
the guy in and you go to court as the complainant. Right?
But no junkie is going to be a complainant against a pusher.
He *loves* that pusher, that's the guy who gives him his fix.
So the cops have to take the pusher in. But the rules on
how we can seize evidence are unbelievable. Most people
wouldn't believe it. Listen, a few months ago we get word
from an informant that there's a lot of junk in an apartment in Queens. We get a warrant from a judge, go into
the apartment, find six kilos of heroin—that's over thirteen
pounds—and a lot of laboratory equipment. Now, with
that much junk and the equipment this has to be a very
big, well-financed, well-organized operation. We arrest the
guy in the apartment and the case goes to court. Not to
trial, but to a preliminary hearing to suppress the evidence
—on the grounds that it was illegally seized. That's par for
the course. They always try a suppression hearing. So we
show the warrant we had. And the defense wants to know
if the warrant was legally issued. It was issued on the
strength of information from an informant. But, says the

defense lawyer, was the informant known to be reliable? Because after all you can't go busting into someone's apartment because just anyone says it's loaded with junk. And the fact that the apartment *did* turn out to have all that junk in it isn't acceptable proof of the stool's reliability.

"So the defense lawyer wants to know if the stool had given us information before that produced convictions. And the DA says that he did, twice in fact. But, asks the defense lawyer, had the convictions been handed down at the time the warrant was issued? In other words, was the informant at the moment when the warrant was issued known to be reliable? And the answer is no. When the warrant was issued, the convictions weren't in yet. We had them at the time of this hearing, you understand, but not when the warrant was issued. So the judge says the warrant was illegal and that we seized the evidence illegally. So the guy goes free. Not even a trial.

"And lots of times the pusher never even gets to a suppression hearing, much less a trial. The courts have so many unsettled cases that the judges and the DA's agree with each other to reduce felony charges to misdemeanors just to help clear the calendars. So some pushers end up pleading guilty to minor charges like mere possession, and drawing maybe six months—sometimes less than their addict customers get for possession of a hypodermic needle. That's one of the reasons why it's so easy to be a pusher. Even a little street-corner pusher can make close to $1,000 a day. If he's smart and careful he can keep at it for years before he gets busted. And when he *is* caught—let's say after three years—he knows that all this search-and-seizure razzle-dazzle in the court is probably going to let him beat the case. And even if he doesn't beat it, and it's his first offense, and he can't cop out to a misdemeanor, he'll still get away with maybe three years in jail. So for the whole six years—three on the street dealing, three in jail—he comes out with an average income of about $150,000 a year, untaxed. Not bad."

"Look," Hotchner said. "My partner and I are making meets with some more stools tomorrow. You want to come? You could just be a third cop along. You might learn something."

I said I'd like to.

Chapter 16

The next morning I met Hotchner at the Narcotics Bureau headquarters on the second floor of the station house at Old Slip and South Street in downtown Manhattan. The building was old and dusty and detectives milled around the partitioned offices, some meeting their partners for the day's work, some getting ready to go to court, many typing out reports. Hotchner was again looking very collegiate, wearing the same cord jacket but with a tan V-neck sweater under it. He introduced me to his partner, a man named Robins, and we went out and got into Hotchner's Volkswagen. Robins was quiet, about forty-five, heavy-set—a perfect complement to the eager young Hotchner.

"We use our own cars," Hotchner explained. "Department cars are too easy to make—to spot—and sometimes it's more convenient to use your own anyway. We don't get an allowance for it, but that's the way things go sometimes. Before we meet the stools we've got a little business up in Harlem. There's a *botánica* up there—you know what that is? Where the Puerto Ricans buy herbs and candles and voodoo stuff and whatnot. Well, there's a *botánica* up there that's dealing *bombitas* like there's no tomorrow. It's out of our territory, but the guys who work up there have all been made so we're going to take a look at it. We raided it a while ago and the owner is awaiting trial, but he's a real smart cookie. He needs money for a good lawyer and he knows that if we hit him again the second charge will just be lumped in with the first and it won't make that much difference. In fact, it'll even give his lawyer a chance to argue that we're harassing him, that for some sinister reason we're out to get him. So he just keeps on dealing. And he's right. We don't want to hit again, for just those reasons, but we figure we'll go up and angel off some of his customers. Angeling off is when you know someone's dealing and you lay back some place and bust the customers coming out. Sometimes you do it to get information on exactly where the dealer is and sometimes you do it, like this time, just to make business rough for him."

We parked the car next to a school in Spanish Harlem, and Hotchner said, "Now, you see across the intersection there, about five stores down from the far corner, the place with the red sign in front, that's the place." I squinted and could just make out the sign.

We sat for five minutes and then Robins said, "If he comes right back out he's dirty." I hadn't seen anyone go in, but in a moment I saw something move under the sign. "Here he comes," Hotchner said. The man came into view then, crossing the street. He was tall and thin and walking very fast. When he got to the car, Hotchner and Robins stepped out. They touched his arm and walked him into a doorway. We heard a crunching sound. Hotchner stooped down.

"There it is," he said, pointing to a few bits of broken glass and a small damp area on the pavement. "He stepped on it. You're a smart guy, aren't you? So smart you're all strung out. Let me see your arms." The man pulled up his left sleeve. His arm was covered with sores, many of them open and running. "Cover it up," Hotchner said, making a face, "and get the hell out of here."

We got back in the car. "I'm getting married in three months," Hotchner said, "and when my kids are old enough to know anything I'm going to bring them up here and show them what a real, strung-out junkie looks like. And then if I ever hear them even so much as say the word 'pot' I'm going to wale the hell out of them."

"Here come two," Robins said.

"I didn't see," Hotchner said. "They come out of the store?" The sidewalks were filled with pedestrians, but Hotchner had no trouble spotting the men Robins was talking about.

The two men, actually they were about eighteen, crossed the street and started across the schoolyard. Hotchner and Robins got out and walking fast made it to the other end of the yard before the men did. They stepped into a hallway and waited.

"They use the basements in these buildings to get off in," Hotchner explained. "They'll probably come in here or one of the buildings next door."

The men reached the end of the schoolyard, crossed the street, and walked into our hallway. Hotchner and Robins grabbed them. Robins took one aside and searched him. Hotchner looked at the other.

"Man, you are shaking like anything," he said. "When someone shakes like that it only means one thing, and you know what that is. You're dirty, aren't you?"

The man shook his head.

"Look, I know you're dirty. Where is it?"

The man shrugged and looked at his feet. "In there," he said, nodding at a cigarette pack in his shirt pocket.

"Hand it to me," Hotchner said.

The man gave it to him, and inside Hotchner found two nickel bags and a *bombita*. "You get the *bombita* at the *botánica* over there?"

The man nodded.

Robins's man was clean. Robins and Hotchner took the other one in and booked him. (The next morning in court he was released. The legal aid defending him argued successfully that the defendant, when he saw his friend being searched by Robins, might have reasonably concluded that

the two men were detectives. If he did think Hotchner was
a detective, then his admission to him that he was carrying
drugs was perhaps made out of fear of Hotchner's authority. That is, the man was coerced into making the admission. Coercion, of course, is unconstitutional, and the man
was released. On his way out he asked Hotchner for fifteen
cents to get a subway token for the ride back to Harlem.
Hotchner gave it to him. "That guy shouldn't have walked
out of here," Hotchner said as we left court. "I'm not saying he should have been jailed, but he should have been
forced into a hospital. If he had typhoid, they'd force him
into a hospital, right?")

After the man had been booked, we got back into the
Volkswagen and drove downtown to the Museum of Natural History. The museum, because it sits on the banks of
the West Side narcotics stream, made a good meeting place
for narcos and stools. We stopped at the door and a young
man walked out, quickly took the two steps to the car,
and slid into the back seat next to Robins.

"How's it going, Billy?" Hotchner asked, twisting around
in his seat behind the wheel.

"Not too bad, man, not too bad." He was colored, about
twenty-five. "I checked out that guy over on 82nd Street
for you—you know, in the house there between Columbus
and Amsterdam, and, man, somebody must have beat you
there 'cause there ain't no action there at all, man, nothin'."

Robins took out a small notebook and wrote in it briefly.
"You know a guy named Manuel, a tall guy, Spanish?"
he asked.

"Where's he work?"

"Around 96th Street."

"Manuel . . . Manuel . . . let's see. A tall guy? Wears a black jacket all the time? He in action?"

"Could you cop off him?"

"I guess so, if he's dealin'. I didn't know he was dealin'. I'll check on that for you."

"How about that lunch place uptown?"

The stool's face fell in apology. "Man, I couldn't get up there. You know I been tryin' to get welfare and it's comin' through this week and then, you know, I won't have to hustle so bad and I can get around a little. So I'll check it, I'll check it."

"What about Freddy? You see him at all?"

"Freddy, yeah, he's back goin' again. I can score from him if you want him. But you just busted him. He just got out."

"We're not particular," Hotchner said. "We don't mind busting the same guy twice."

"Oh, somethin' else, you guys care about pot?"

"What's the weight?"

"Maybe a pound, couple of pounds."

"We never turn down a few pounds of pot."

They talked about how to set up the connection selling marijuana, and then Hotchner and Robins set another date with the stool. He got out and we drove off.

"Not all stools are that easy to work with," Robins explained. "The guy we're going to see now is a real bastard. This guy wants something for nothing. You'll see what I mean when we talk to him."

We pulled up to the curb at a phone booth on Ninth Avenue in the fifties. A tall, goateed Negro got in. The detectives had already explained to me that the man, a marijuana pusher in his forties, lived in an apartment with several teen-age girls. He made a lot of money selling pot and enjoyed turning on the girls and their friends. He could also get hold of heroin if someone—particularly one of the girls—sounded curious about it. From his first words, he seemed unconvinced that he really had to send some people to jail to avoid jail himself.

"We don't want any more wild-goose chases like last night," Hotchner started.

"But, man, that wasn't my fault. How could I know he gave me the wrong address? I thought I had the right address, man. That ain't my fault. What can I do?"

"You can call the guy up now, tell him you're ready to buy the stuff and to have it ready for you. Then we get a warrant and go in and there it is. Right? Easy?" Hotchner was trying to sound firm but friendly, like a parent with a naughty child.

"Right now? Call him now?"

"Now, from that booth there."

The pusher squirmed. "Man, you want me to turn in my friend."

Hotchner feigned a look of shock. "You are *so* right. I mean, that's the name of the game, right? Why we're all here? I'm a cop, remember? And you push pot and that's illegal and you've been caught and you don't want to go to jail."

"I know all that, man. I ain't dumb. But, man, what can

I do? What's that judge gonna expect of me? I'm human, you know?"

Hotchner began to feel he was wasting his time. He reached into the back seat and opened the door next to the pusher. "Look," he said, "why don't you just get out and forget it. You just sit around and then when we go to court I'll tell the judge what happened, about all this great cooperation we got from you, and then you can just take your chances on what he'll say. My guess is that he'll say something like three years."

"Okay, you win, I'll call." He went to the sidewalk booth, spoke into the phone, and returned to the car. "He's comin' down. I'll see him in half an hour and set it up and meet you back here, in an hour."

Hotchner agreed. We went back in an hour, but the pusher never showed up. "I figured he wouldn't," Hotchner said, and Robins nodded in agreement.

"Actually, we aren't really too sorry he didn't come through for us this time," Robins said. "We're waiting for him to get really up tight in this situation, which he will when the court day gets close. He's in with a guy we want. You ever hear the name Little Tony? He's the biggest supplier on the West Side. He lives on the East Side, but he has dealers working for him all the way from Greenwich Village up to Harlem—Duffy Square, 71st Street, 82nd Street, 96th Street. He's a big man, and this guy here we just had in the car deals for him. So we figure if we can make him nervous enough about what's going to happen to him in court he might get desperate and spill something.

So every time he doesn't come through for us on something like this thing today it gives us a little more leverage."

The inside of the Volkswagen suddenly seemed very
cramped. I didn't know if I should tell them I had heard
of Little Tony or not. I was afraid if I did I might end up
getting Bobby or Helen in trouble, so I decided to keep
quiet.

"This Little Tony is a bad guy," Hotchner was saying.
"You've seen how Helen and those junkies live. You should
see how this guy lives, the kind of living he gets off them.
He has an apartment in the East 60s, lots of girls, goes
out all the time, eats in the best restaurants, has a real fine
time. And the best of it is he's got lots of friends don't have
the slightest idea where he gets his dough. He tells them
real estate or something like that."

"They should only know," Robins said.

"How do you know so much about him?" I asked.

"Man," said Hotchner, "we know *all* about him. That
guy hasn't been without a tail, I mean a narco tail, in . . ."
He looked at Robins. "How long, Charlie, how long's it
been now?"

"Oh, at least nine months, maybe longer," Robins said.
"We know everything he does, but getting something on
him, I mean something good, is another story. That guy is
so careful. He never even *sees* any junk. He wouldn't know
a nickel bag if one dropped down in front of him. Everything's done through other guys. A real sharp character.
And he looks real clean, too. Until you take a look at his
yellow sheet, which is four pages, all the way back to when

he was thirteen. Assault, armed robbery, manslaughter. He did a lot of time for the Mafia and never ratted and I guess about two, three years ago he really made it with them and now this is his bit, all this West Side junk."

"What are you doing tomorrow night?" Hotchner asked me.

"Nothing special."

"Come with me. Little Tony's going to Frederick's, the discothèque. He goes there every Wednesday night, he owns a piece of it, and I'll be there watching. You can come and get a look at the great man yourself."

Chapter 17

Crosstown from Bob and Helen's West Side junk world, insulated from it by Central Park, Fifth Avenue, Madison Avenue, and Park Avenue, on a quiet tree-lined street in the fifties, sits Frederick's—on the outside spotlighted, canopied, and courted by cabs, on the inside dark and elegant. Hotchner was at a small table near the far wall, about three tables removed from the dance floor. The music was recorded stereo, bellowing from unseen speakers, augmented by three Beatle-haired boys playing drums, vibes, and bass. The floor was choked with fruggers and jerkers and monkeyers. Hotchner was with a young, pretty brunette whom he introduced as his fiancée. He ordered drinks, calling the waiter by name.

"You seem to come here a lot," I said.

"I do because he does," Hotchner shouted back over the noise, and tilted his head just slightly toward the dance floor. I started to turn but Hotchner put a hand on my arm. "In a minute," he said.

"I'm glad to see the police department pays its detectives so well," I said, raising a drink.

The girl laughed, and Hotchner said, "The shield pays for everything in here. It may look swish, but the guys who own it are no great bargains, so they figure it's good business to let the fuzz ride for free. This way if we make a bust we lead the bad guys out gracefully instead of dragging them across the dance floor in handcuffs." His eyes glanced past my shoulder and then settled on his drink. "Now," he said.

I turned in the chair. People at the two tables next to ours had gotten up to dance, leaving a clear view of Little Tony. He was sitting with another man, who had his back to us, and three young girls. He was a little on the short side, but strongly built, and good-looking in clothes that had a curious Madison Avenue style to them. Two of the girls were giggling with Tony. The other girl and the man sat sullenly drinking from Manhattan glasses. They said something to each other, and then the man turned from the girl angrily, exposing his profile to us. It was Santo.

"Hey, I know that guy," I said without thinking, and was instantly sorry.

"You *know* him," Hotchner said, amazed.

"Well, maybe not," I said.

The detective thought for a couple of minutes and then said, "Look, that's one of Tony's cutters, and if you *do* know him you'd better tell me. Because they are very rough people. And I know you wouldn't *want* to do anything to hurt yourself or to hurt any of the junkies you know, but sometimes a man's ignorance can hurt him without him knowing it till it's too late. So don't try to figure the angles yourself. You might end up hurting someone. For example, if he does know you from some junkies and he sees you here with me . . . well, he's gonna start thinking all kinds of things, and those are the kind of guys who don't wait for proof. Just a little suspicion and they don't think twice about slipping some junkie a hotshot. . . ."

"Let's go," I said.

We walked up Lexington Avenue to the Mayflower Coffee Shop.

"Okay," Hotchner said when we were settled at a table, "let's hear it."

"I do know him. I suppose it's no secret to you that Bobby's dealing."

"It's no secret to me that *any* junkie is dealing. They all deal, at one time or another."

"Well, Bobby has the idea he can take the Needle Park business away from Little Tony, and he's been talking Santo into selling him a few pieces now and then. And once when I was with Bobby we met Santo and he introduced me. That's how I know him."

"Where were you when you met him?"

"I can't tell you that."

"All right. But you know if Santo had seen you in there tonight he'd have figured you were working with me and that Bobby had set him up, and that would have been the end of Bobby, so hereafter let me do the thinking, don't take anything for granted. Now you don't want to tell me where you met Santo. Okay. But do you have any idea why Santo should be selling pieces to Bobby, instead of to his boss, Little Tony, when there is one helluva panic on and people are practically committing murder in the streets for that stuff?"

"Not really, I figured he'd talked Santo into it, was maybe paying him more money than Little Tony."

"Look, you could get yourself and your junkie friends in a lot of trouble. You're brushing up against some people who've been at this game for years. They don't just do things for a junkie because they've been talked into it. And Bobby could never, not in a million years, pay more than Tony because Tony is the Mafia, and that's like all the money in the world. In addition to which Santo works for the Mafia too, so it's not even his stuff anyway, it's theirs to begin with. There's a lot you don't know. I'll tell you why Santo is dealing to Bobby. Remember I said in the Automat that when a junkie gets busted he rats on a couple of connections to get an SS—a suspended sentence? Well, when a dealer or a wholesaler gets busted he naturally doesn't want to get locked up any more than a junkie does, so he wants to play the same game. But it's a lot harder for him because he can't rat on another Mafia dealer, and who the hell else is there? There aren't any independents, to speak of. So Tony figures that when he gets busted, if he does, he'll have Bobby all set up in business to rat on. And he needs that kind of scapegoat, especially now during this panic when junkies like Helen are looking to rat on every connection they know. Some of those connections are going to rat on their suppliers, and Little Tony knows that if this panic keeps up, sooner or later one of his men is gonna get busted and rat on him. It has to happen, and he knows it. Maybe without this panic he wouldn't have figured he needed Bobby in business bad enough to let him take over in Needle Park. But with the panic it's good business. It's like insurance. He may not like it, but he'd be crazy not to protect himself. And what's he giving Bobby, anyway? Needle Park. Big deal. He's got the whole West Side. To him Needle Park is a drop in the bucket."

I told Hotchner I thought I'd better get home.

"Okay, he said. "If you hear anything else, though, call me, will you? Don't take anything for granted. Your ignorance can end up killing someone—maybe you." He was smiling when he said, "Maybe you."

I took a cab back to the Martell and was crossing the sidewalk to go in when I heard someone call from the corner. It was Bobby. He came running up from the corner.

"I thought you were in jail," I said.

"Not me—Helen. She got busted, about an hour ago. It's bad, man. Selling. They say they got an observation on her. And not even narcos, man, just a couple of plainclothesmen. They say they watched her make a sale to Sammy and they busted Sammy too, so like if he says he bought off her then like that's that. She'll go away a long, long, long time. 'Cause you know she's got this three-year SS from the last time and like they'll lay that on her too. So I don't know . . . I don't know. That's where it's at, man. Real tight."

"What happened to you?" I asked.

"Discon. Helen said she told you. The judge threw it out. He said the cop never should have busted me while I was in the phone booth. Like how could I be disorderly if I was just standing in the booth talking to someone on the phone? Which is right. The cop was a real jerk. But Helen's in real trouble, man."

"Can't Hotchner help her?" I asked.

"Maybe he could have, if he'd been there. Like he could have stood up for her with the plainclothesman, but she's been booked now, she's in the House of D right now, so what can he do? It's got to go to court now, and when the judge sees that SS, man, that's all. That's it. Goodbye Helen."

"Well, I've got to get some sleep. I'll see you later, Bobby."

I went up to the room and called Hotchner at home. He wasn't back yet. I waited fifteen minutes, then called again. Hotchner answered and I told him about Helen. Hotchner sounded almost pleased to hear she had been busted. He said he'd see what he could do.

It was 5 a.m. when I went to sleep. When I got up eight

hours later Helen was already out of jail. How she got out, and what happened in the next two weeks, I know only from hearsay, by piecing together accounts from Bobby, Helen, Hotchner, and other junkies and narcos.

Hotchner had gone down to the Criminal Courts building at nine o'clock that morning. He went up to Part 1B on the fourth floor, where most of the drug cases were handled, and found the plainclothesman that busted Helen. He talked with him a moment, then dug up the assistant district attorney who handled narcotics cases, and talked to him. By the time Helen's case was called at eleven o'clock everything had been fixed. The ADA told the judge that Hotchner knew Helen, that she had worked for him as an informer in the past, and that she was in a position to be helpful in an investigation then in progress, an investigation into the activities of a Mafia narcotics man named Anthony Rizzetto, alias Little Tony. The judge adjourned the case for a month and set bail for $100, which Hotchner promptly supplied.

He walked with Helen through the courtroom's swinging doors into the dim corridor crowded with detectives, tearful families, and defendants, most of them boys in their teens and early twenties. Helen threw her arms around Hotchner and gave him a hug. That drew a cheer and cries of "Way to go, Hotch!" from other narcos in the hall. He took her by the arm and led her to the elevator and out of the building.

"You know damned well, Helen," he said when they were walking up the sidewalk in the sun, "that I didn't do this out of the goodness of my heart. I've got a job for you to do."

She turned off the warmth. "Did any cop *ever* do anything out of the goodness of his heart?" she asked bitterly.

"What heart?" Hotchner said, letting her know she wasn't getting any place. "In here," he said, guiding her into a bar a block north of the court building.

"It's a little early for a drink, isn't it?" she said.

"You're not going to have a drink. You're just going to talk, baby, that's all, just talk." They sat down at a back table. "You want to do about ten years for that sale and another three on your SS?" he asked.

"Come off it, Hotchner. You may look smart in your college clothes and your big tall strong physique but it doesn't pull anything with me at all. So don't get smart. You know damned well I don't want to do time. Any time. Not one day or one week or anything."

"Then you're going to work for me."

"Haven't I *been* working for you, baby? I mean, what the hell is this, anyway, some kind of game or something? Who's given you every decent collar you've had in the past four weeks? Answer me. Who?"

"I'm not talking about simple little corner pushers, Helen. I'm talking about something else."

"What else?"

"Little Tony."

"Little Tony!" She shouted the words, lifting half out of her chair. "Little Tony. Are you kidding? I never laid *eyes* on Little Tony. Little Tony. You *are* crazy."

"Or Bobby."

She held up a hand. "Now wait a minute, buddy. You're not pinning anything on Bobby."

"Listen, Helen. You know as well as I do that Bobby's dealing all over Needle Park. In fact, for the past few weeks he's been just about the *only* guy dealing in Needle Park. He's taken over all of Little Tony's business there."

"Well, *I* certainly don't know anything about *that*," she said, sitting back with an attitude that said she knew but wasn't going to talk.

"Look, Helen. I'll put it on the line. You're looking into ten, fifteen years right now, and you're not getting that knocked down by helping me bust just any cheap street dealer. Not five or ten of them. You know that. Now if you want to just stay out on bail for a month and then walk into court with nothing going for you, that's your business. I couldn't care less. But don't cry *after* you're locked up, honey, because then it'll be too late. If you want to do something, you've got to do it now, and you've got to give me something big, because you know as well as I do that no judge is going to want to even *listen* to anything from you that isn't big."

"All right. But what can I do? I don't even *know* Little Tony."

"Helen, you can get me Little Tony if you want to. I know you can. You know people who cut for him. You can get him if you want to."

She sat up straight in the chair and let out a long, despairing sigh. "Yeah," she said. "I guess I could. . . . But he'd kill me. He's Mafia and they don't mess around. I mean, ratting on a regular pusher is one thing. He'll see you when he gets out of jail and probably by then he has other problems and he's not going to go up on you. But Little Tony. I wouldn't even have to wait till he got out. One of his friends would finish me so fast I'd look like a . . . like a . . . honey, they'd smear me all over Broadway and then scrape up the mess and feed it to their girlfriends' poodles."

"Then don't bother with Tony. There's Bobby. One way or the other we'll get them all, Helen. You set up Bobby for me and let *him* rat on Tony. He will, you know. He'll have to. He won't do time, Helen. He'll rat on Tony and Tony will do all the time for both of you."

"Yeah," she said. "And what about his friends?"

"What about your ten or fifteen years?"

Neither said anything for five minutes.

Then Helen said, "Okay. I'll give you Bobby."

Chapter 18

At 3 a.m. two weeks later Helen stood with Hank in the darkness next to the Manufacturers Hanover Trust Company branch at Essex and Delancey Streets on the Lower East Side. Diagonally across Delancey Street from them was the corner where Bobby always went to get a cab after picking up his bundles from Santo's or from the alley where he kept them stashed. The corner was flooded with light from a hot-dog and frozen-custard stand. A few feet off the corner, next to the BMT subway entrance, a blind newsdealer sold papers and magazines from a kiosk.

"He should be here at about 3:15," Helen said. "It never takes him more than ten minutes to get here from Santo's or the stash. He'll be coming from Santo's tonight. He told me he had got two more pieces from Santo and they were cutting them tonight. There won't be any trouble. They'll just bust him quietly when he steps into the light and then we can go over and clean out the stash and we're set. That's all. The narcos don't know where the stash is. They don't even know there *is* a stash. There's no problem. We'll get the stash"—she put an arm around Hank and smiled up at him through the darkness—"and then you can be the biggest dealer on the West Side, Hank. Bobby'll rat on Little Tony and you can move in. It'll all be open."

"Except for Bobby."

"Hank, you know this job takes heart, and let's face it, Bobby hasn't got it. Bobby'll never have it. Like all his life, no matter what he's tried to do, there's always been someone around a couple of jumps ahead of him. I know he's your brother, but let's face it. He never knows if the sun is up or down or what. I can handle him. He does what I tell him to do. He'll have to be around but it'll be you handling the business, Hank."

Traffic was heavy on Delancey Street, trucks and cars barreling into it from the Manhattan Bridge. A couple of men stood at the counter in the hot-dog stand, slowly eating frozen custard and staring emptily out to the street.

That night I had gone again with Bobby to Santo's. When we left, he hid two manila envelopes in the back of the alley—taking pains to insure that he was not observed —and stuffed another smaller one under his shirt next to the gun he had carried since he was robbed, and started west on Stanton Street. We turned left on Essex, walked through the blackness next to the huge one-story brick public market, now closed for the night, and then quickly strode into the light at the hot-dog stand on the corner. Bobby was raising his hand at a cab when someone said, "Stop right there!"

"Not this time!" Bobby shouted back, and pulled out his gun.

Facing the cab, I heard three quick explosions and turned toward Bobby. He was lying on the sidewalk covered by four men, one of whom wore a newsdealer's white change apron.

"Get off him! Get the hell off him! He's shot!" It was Hotchner and he was pulling the other detectives off Bobby. Bobby, the front of his white shirt ripped by bullets and soaked with blood from the collar down to his belt, looked up at Hotchner.

"I saw you, man. I saw you. Why'd you shoot? You didn't have to shoot me, I saw you, I wasn't gonna shoot." He turned onto his side and held his hands over his chest. Hotchner bent over him. A crowd was around them and people were yelling to call an ambulance. A uniformed cop tried to keep them back. A priest came out of the crowd and bent with Hotchner over Bobby, who had stopped moving.

Then the priest walked away and Hotchner reached into Bobby's bloody shirt and pulled out the envelope. The bullets had torn it open and the white powder where it spilled from the bags was red with blood. He bent over and picked up Bobby's gun from the gutter. Then he saw me. "You should have told me he carried this," he said.

"You should have told me you were going to grab him here," I said.

The ambulance finally came and took him away.

Across the street by the bank, Helen heard the shots and saw Bobby fall. She started toward him. Hank grabbed her arm, but she had already stopped. "Bobby," she said under her breath, and then backed up slowly into the darkness again. They watched the men around Bobby, and when they saw the priest stand up and walk away, Helen said, "He's finished." She said it not as she had spoken Bobby's name, but matter of factly, as if giving a stranger the time. She wiped her nose.

"Come on," she said to Hank. "I'm sick. I need something. Let's get that stash."

Chapter 19

After the shooting neither Bobby nor Helen saw Needle Park again, at least not for long. Bobby was in the Bellevue Hospital prison ward for six weeks, and was booked there for felonious possession of narcotics and felonious assault on a police officer (for having drawn the gun). He agreed to tell Hotchner what he knew about Little Tony and Santo —Santo's cutting room was raided after that, but Santo had left for Mexico and all the detectives got was the equipment —and the charges were reduced to simple assault and non-felonious possession. He was sentenced to six months on Riker's Island.

Helen and Hank got the stash, stayed stoned for four

days in a hotel room on the Lower East Side, lost the rest of the drug to another junkie who grabbed it while they were on the nod, and then headed uptown to Needle Park.

When I saw Helen she hadn't eaten for four days and had slept only intermittently between shots. Hotchner was looking for her to find out what she knew about Santo and to remind her that her month was almost gone and she had a court date coming up. He never found her. She jumped bail and took a bus to the Lexington hospital, where she knew she would be reasonably safe. The hospital never revealed who the new patients were, and if you were wanted some place it was a good place to hole up, get off drugs, take a rest, and get back into shape for the next round. After she had been there for three weeks I got a letter from her saying she had put me on the list of people she wanted to write to and that she had asked her doctor to write to me too. Two days later I received a letter from him.

"Helen has spoken much about you," he wrote, "and I have concluded that you knew her quite well. She has asked that I write and advise you of her condition. I do this only at her insistence.

"As you may have guessed, addiction with her—as with many addicts—is less a disease than a symptom. I mean, she has emotional problems much more broad and severe than the addiction itself and which no doubt are the cause of the addiction. She has a severe character disorder and a strong compulsion to dominate whomever she associates with. She has a strong need to have someone to dominate, and for the past few years that someone has evidently been her boyfriend Bobby. From talking to her I would be willing to hazard the guess that he himself is a predominantly passive individual who feels as strong a need to be dominated by Helen as she does to dominate him. I would say that there was little hope for a total rehabilitation unless they are separated, as they no doubt reinforce each other's weaknesses."

Over the next two months I corresponded regularly with the doctor, taking his advice on when to write to Helen and what to send her. He seemed to grow more and more interested in her case, and that gave us something in common. When she had been in Lexington for two months I received this letter from her, typed entirely in capitals:

REC'D YOUR TELEGRAM YESTERDAY—THANKS SO MUCH FOR THE $5.00, I REALLY NEEDED IT. FARRELL (THE GUY WHO WAS LIVING IN THE ROOM YOU FIRST MET ME IN) HAS BEEN SENDING ME A LITTLE CASH, BUT NOT ENOUGH TO REALLY HELP OUT. HE IS AFRAID I WILL ACCUMULATE ENOUGH TO LEAVE HERE. I REALLY WISH HE WOULDN'T INSULT MY INTELLIGENCE SO. IF I WANTED TO LEAVE HERE A THING LIKE "NECESSARY FUNDS" WOULDN'T STOP ME—AT LEAST THIS TIME I WOULD HAVE CLOTHES TO WEAR OUT—NO MORE "BLANKET" DESIGNS! (SMILE.) ANYWAY, I'M GETTING ALONG TOO WELL HERE TO THINK ABOUT LEAVING YET. AS FAR AS MY JOB IS CONCERNED, I LIKE IT WELL ENOUGH, AND I HAVE A NICE BOSS—A WOMAN! AND BELIEVE IT OR NOT WE GET ALONG WELL. I AM WORKING IN "Y" BUILDING IN THE PURCHASING DEPARTMENT.

I RECEIVED A LETTER FROM BOBBY & HE IS GOING TO

COME DOWN HERE WHEN HE FINISHES HIS TIME ON RIK-
ER'S— (ALSO HE HAS NO MONEY, YOU KNOW HOW I FEEL
ABOUT HIM—I WOULD RATHER SEE HIM WITH A FEW
DOLLARS, THAN MYSELF—IF WORSE COMES TO WORSE, I
CAN WASH & IRON FOR SOME COMMISSARY, BUT HE HAS A
RATHER TOUGH TIME HUSTLING ANYTHING WHERE HE
IS.) — (IN FACT, HE HAS A HARD TIME HUSTLING ANY
TIME, LAZY AS HE IS.) I AM VERY PLEASED ABOUT HIS DE-
CISION TO COME DOWN HERE. ON RIKER'S ALL THE GUYS
TALK ABOUT IS WHEN THEY GET OUT, HOW THEY ARE GO-
ING TO GET HIGH—IT CERTAINLY IS "ADVERSE THERAPY"
AND I FEEL THAT BOBBY IS TOO SUSCEPTIBLE TO THAT—
(AS I WOULD BE.)

SOMETIMES I WISH I COULD SEE YOU. NOW THAT I LOOK
BACK, WE HAD QUITE A FEW LAUGHS! REMEMBER THE
NIGHT YOU CAME OVER AND BOBBY HAD ALL THAT COFFEE
THERE AND I WAS SO STONED I COULDN'T GET A HIT?—I
SURE WAS "OUT OF IT." IT SEEMS LIKE A MILLION YEARS
AGO. THE DIFFERENCE BETWEEN NOW AND BEFORE IS
LIKE NIGHT AND DAY. EVERYTHING THAT HAPPENED BE-
FORE SEEMS VERY HAZY AND ALMOST LIKE A DREAM
SOMETIMES, OR LIKE SOMETHING THAT HAPPENED EONS
AGO. STRANGE, IT IS ONLY A MATTER OF A FEW MONTHS.
I'M SO "CLEAN" NOW I CAN'T STAND MYSELF—(I'M
ONLY KIDDING). ALTHOUGH, AFTER BEING ACCUSTOMED
TO BEING "HIGH" FOR SO LONG, IT DOES SEEM STRANGE TO
HAVE MY "WAKE-UP" A "CUP OF COFFEE." I AM REALLY
JUST "COMING AROUND" NOW. IT TAKES AT LEAST 3–5
MONTHS TO GET BACK TO "NORMAL" (IF THAT IS WHAT

YOU WERE IN THE FIRST PLACE, PERSONALLY I THINK I
HAVE ALWAYS BEEN SICK, SICK, SICK, BUT THAT'S AN-
OTHER STORY.) SERIOUSLY, THOUGH, IT'S THE STRANGEST
THING IN THE WORLD, HOW MUCH ONE'S THINKING PAT-
TERN CHANGES WHEN YOU COME OFF DRUGS—YOUR
SENSE OF VALUES CHANGES CONSIDERABLY. AT FIRST
YOU'RE TOO "SICK" TO THINK OF ANYTHING EXCEPT
"MEDICATION" AND EVEN FOR A MONTH OR SO AFTER
KICKING, YOU ARE STILL ACHING AND FEELING EXHAUSTED
AND TIRED. (I THINK THAT'S WHY SO MANY TIMES I HAVE
GONE RIGHT BACK, BECAUSE I WASN'T PHYSICALLY WELL
AND OF COURSE STUFF PACIFIED EVERYTHING.—THEN,
DURING THE FIRST COUPLE OF MONTHS YOU BECOME CON-
FUSED ABOUT EVERYTHING, AND AFTER THAT YOU GRAD-
UALLY SEE EVERYTHING FALL INTO PLACE LIKE THE
PIECES OF A PUZZLE). YOU FINALLY START TO THINK
"AHEAD" (WHICH IS SOMETHING THAT IS IMPOSSIBLE AT
FIRST). I MAY NOT BE MAKING MYSELF CLEAR—BUT—
I'M TRYING TO. JUST LISTEN TO THE WAY I'M TALKING—!
AND I HAVEN'T EVEN STARTED THERAPY YET!!! I SUPPOSE
IT WOULD BE IMPOSSIBLE FOR YOU TO COME DOWN AND
VISIT ME, BUT I WOULD REALLY LOVE TO SEE YOU— (I
KNOW THAT YOU HAVE NEVER SEEN ME BE REALLY SERI-
OUS, AND YOU ARE PROBABLY THINKING, "WHAT DOES SHE
WANT, OR WHAT IS SHE TRYING TO CON OUT OF ME?" BUT
REALLY I'M SERIOUS . . . I GUESS BECAUSE I HAVE LIVED
FOR SO LONG "ON THE CON" THAT I FIND SINCERITY QUITE
UNNATURAL FOR ME, BUT WHEN I'M NOT STRUNG OUT IS
THE ONLY TIME THAT I REALIZE HOW MUCH OF A PHONY

I AM WHEN I'M USING, AND I GUESS I HAVE SORT OF A COMPLEX ABOUT IT. I THINK I TOLD YOU ONCE, I DON'T LIKE MYSELF VERY MUCH WHEN I USE, BECAUSE IT MAKES SUCH AN ANIMAL OUT OF ME . . . STRANGE, HOW PEOPLE ARE ONLY INSTRUMENTS TO ATTAIN SOMETHING WHEN I'M STRUNG OUT, AND EVEN STRANGER, YOU ARE THE ONLY EXCEPTION TO THAT RULE SINCE I'M USING. MAYBE IT'S BECAUSE I RESPECT YOU—BEING THAT YOU AREN'T A TRICK OR REALLY IN ANY WAY INVOLVED IN THAT LIFE OTHER THAN JUST INTEREST.

I'M IN A TALKATIVE MOOD NOW, AND IT'S NOT TOO OFTEN THAT I'M LIKE THAT. BEFORE, WHEN I WAS ON BOMBITAS IT WAS A PHONY ENTHUSIASM I FELT AND THAT'S THE REASON I WAS SO TALKATIVE, BUT WHEN I'M NORMAL I'M USUALLY QUIET. I GUESS THE REASON I'M SO GABBY NOW IS BECAUSE I ENJOY WRITING TO YOU. WRITING LETTERS REALLY ISN'T MY STICK WHEN I'M IN JAIL. I WILL WRITE OCCASIONALLY WHEN I'M ON THE STREET AND THERE IS REALLY SOMETHING TO TALK ABOUT. BUT IN HERE MOSTLY EVERY DAY IS THE SAME AND VERY LITTLE EXCITEMENT. QUITE A CHANGE FROM THE WAY I LIVED IN N.Y. (NEVER A DULL MOMENT) AND OF COURSE I HAVEN'T QUITE THE NERVE IN HERE I HAD ON THE STREET, SEEING I HAVE TO LIVE WITH ONLY MY NATURAL "NERVE," WHICH REALLY ISN'T THAT MUCH.

I HAD PLANNED LEAVING IN A COUPLE OF MONTHS, WHEN BOBBY GETS OUT, BUT NOW THAT HE HAS TOLD ME HE IS COMING DOWN HERE, I DON'T KNOW WHEN I AM LEAVING. TO BE QUITE TRUTHFUL, I DON'T QUITE KNOW

WHAT I'M GOING TO DO CONCERNING BOBBY. I DON'T
KNOW WHERE I'M AT WHERE HE IS CONCERNED. WHEN I
FIRST CAME HERE ALL I COULD THINK OF WAS WHEN I
WOULD SEE HIM AGAIN, BUT NOW IT DOESN'T SEEM SO
IMPORTANT. I AM TRYING TO PLAN SOME KIND OF A FU-
TURE FOR MYSELF, BUT WHETHER I AM GOING TO IN-
CLUDE HIM OR NOT IS QUITE A PROBLEM. I KNOW THAT
MAY SEEM STRANGE, BUT WHEN YOU CONSIDER THAT IT
IS HARD FOR TWO JUNKIES (OR EX-JUNKIES) TO MAKE IT
TOGETHER AND CONSIDER THAT I DON'T REALLY KNOW
WHETHER OR NOT I CAN MAKE IT EVEN BY MYSELF . . . ! ?
IT SEEMS LIKE TOO LARGE A DECISION FOR ME TO TACKLE
RIGHT NOW, SO I'M JUST GOING TO PLAY IT BY EAR UNTIL
I FEEL THAT I CAN COME TO THE RIGHT CONCLUSION AS
TO WHAT TO DO WITH MY LIFE. I HAVEN'T SPOKEN (OR
WRITTEN) TO BOBBY ABOUT THIS, AS IT WOULD ONLY
MAKE HIS "TIME" HARDER TO DO . . . HE IS VERY EASILY
UPSET WHEN HE IS IN JAIL, AND I DON'T WANT HIM TO
DO HIS TIME IN THE "HOLE." HE'S DONE THAT BEFORE AS
A RESULT OF SOMETHING I'VE WRITTEN HIM. HE GOES
"OFF," AND THEN OF COURSE HE'S IN TROUBLE. I GUESS
WE ARE ALL SUSCEPTIBLE TO "GOING OFF" WHEN WE GET
UPSETTING NEWS, BUT ESPECIALLY IN JAIL.

BE GOOD. WRITE WHEN YOU GET THE CHANCE. I LOVE
HEARING FROM YOU. TAKE CARE.

Three days later, this letter arrived from the doctor:

"I'm sorry to have to write to tell you that Helen is leaving the hospital against medical advice. She signed the pa-

pers this morning, and will leave tomorrow. I tried for a very long time to convince her to stay; and, when I was unable to, to get her to speak with you by telephone. This she also refused to do. She said that you would convince her to stay, and that she didn't want to stay. But she did say that I could write to you and tell you that she has left.

"I am afraid we weren't able to engage Helen in the program to the degree that would insure her staying here. She could give no good reason for leaving, and I don't really know why she did. It seems that addicts in general find it difficult to tolerate prolonged interpersonal contacts when there is no means of running away from them; at least, it seems to me that this is so. In our setting, one has to face the same people day after day, whether one wishes to or not, and one cannot avoid dealing with people toward whom one has strong feelings, either positive or negative. When this happens, our volunteer patients often leave, and this may be the case with Helen. It is no accident that our patients refer to the world outside as 'the street'; they cherish their mobility, the opportunity to escape difficult relationships, very highly.

"People are inclined to think that psychiatry is an easy field; your patients never die and they never get well. The truth, however, is that they *do* die, some suddenly, by their own hand, and some by inches, like the addict. And when they die, you feel personally responsible. And when they don't, you can never be sure that anything you did contributed to it. It might have happened anyway; given time, it's possible they might have got better by themselves.

"So I feel very bad about Helen. You can always argue that she didn't have sufficient motivation, or sufficient ego strength, or whatever you want to call it. But that is little help, and I prefer to think that we must develop better techniques for treatment, rather than making any excuse for what happens."

A phone call came from Helen the next afternoon. She was in Detroit.

"I just called to say I'm okay, that's all. The doctor said he was going to write to tell you I left, so I thought I'd let you know everything's okay. You hear anything from Bobby?"

She sounded healthy and I was sure she was not back on drugs yet.

"I haven't heard anything from him. He gets out next month. Why did you leave, Helen? You sounded as if you wanted to stay and really clean up."

"I'm clean, baby, and I couldn't stay any longer. I wasn't getting anywhere. I was clean physically and I wasn't getting any therapy, so I left."

"The doctor said he was seeing you."

"Yeah, he was seeing me. But not enough to do anything. That takes years, baby, and I don't have the time. And I was having other troubles. I was making it with this chick in there and Bobby found out about it, someone must have written him, anyway he found out about it, and he was giving me all kinds of noise about it and I can't take that from him, baby, I can't take it. I don't have to take that. And this chick is screaming, too, so I signed myself out. I don't need that. I don't need it. I'm okay. I'm clean, I'm not using . . . I'm okay."

"Where are you getting your money? How did you get to Detroit?"

"I'm hustling, but good tricks, not like those creeps in Needle Park. And I'm going to stop that, too. I'm going to hustle out here to get back on my feet, save some money, and then go back to New York and get a job modeling, or at least working good again, with some good tricks like I used to have. I want to get a good book going like I had before. And these people I'm with now are helping me. They're old friends. I wrote to them and said I wanted to get out and they drove down and got me and brought me back here. They've got good connections, with the right tricks and the cops. They're good people, and they're helping me. What's Bobby going to do when he gets out? I want him out here. If he stays in New York I'll come there and get him, because he needs me and I can help him. But with that thing with Hotchner and Little Tony and Santo I don't think he ought to go back to New York. To tell you the truth, that's really the only thing that's keeping me out of New York. There's a warrant out for me, you know, and if Hotchner saw me it'd be all over. And then I'm not too anxious to spot any of Little Tony's friends either, so I may stay out here awhile. And I want Bobby out here, too. New York would be death for him now. Death. Believe me. So tell him to come out here. I'll come get him or wire him air fare. If you talk to him tell him that."

She called back a couple of weeks later and this time she

was on a nod. She denied it angrily, insisting she had the flu and hadn't slept well for several days. She said she couldn't come to New York to get Bobby and would I mind giving him money for a plane ticket. I told her I had a friend in Detroit who was a psychiatrist and that I had written him and he had agreed to see Bobby, and Helen too if she wanted. This was true. I said I would bring Bobby to Detroit myself. She was delighted.

"I need help," she said. "I know that. I guess I've needed it for a long time. It'll be good for both of us and maybe we can stay clean."

I told the New York City Department of Corrections what I had planned for Bobby—the trip to Detroit, the doctor—and that I was worried what might happen to him in New York if he stayed there and one of Little Tony's men spotted him. They agreed to deliver him to me personally instead of turning him loose at the dock where the ferry tied up from Riker's Island.

So at eleven o'clock on a Saturday morning, exactly four months after he had been sentenced, I parked my car on the northwest corner of 43rd Street and Second Avenue and waited. I had been there about three minutes when Bobby and a uniformed correction officer came walking out of a coffee shop across the street. I got out and walked over to Bobby and we shook hands. The correction officer wished Bobby good luck and left. I asked Bobby if he could stand another cup of coffee.

"Sure," he said, smiling. "Just so long as it doesn't come from Riker's Island." He was wearing prison-release clothes

—dark flannel trousers, denim shirt, blue cotton wind-breaker, black shoes and socks. I had not written to him about going to Detroit, although he had heard by mail from Helen that that was the plan, and that he could see a doctor there if he wanted to. We sat down in a booth and I asked if he was sure he wanted to go.

"Well, to tell you the truth, I don't really know at this point what I want to do. Like I don't know about Helen, is what I really mean, if I should go back with her or not. 'Cause I did a lot of thinking during this last bit and I don't know if we should or not. You know she put me through a lot of changes out there, and maybe . . . Well, like I just don't know. And then, though, there's the thing with the doctor, which I know I should do. I know that's a good chance, getting to see a good doctor for a while, and then I don't want to run into Little Tony, either, so like I say I'm not sure. It's very confusing right now, very, very confusing."

He sat for two or three minutes and then said, "So what do you think I should do?"

I told him he would have to make up his own mind.

"Yeah, that's always been a big part of the trouble, I think. Everyone trying to make up my mind for me—Helen, my mother, my father, my brothers, everyone. I was never much at deciding things."

He sat quietly for a few minutes and then set the coffee cup down on the saucer. "Let's go to Detroit," he said.

We drove out to La Guardia and waited for the flight. We had been sitting for about ten minutes when Bobby said he wanted some gum. He walked around the corner of the waiting room to a newsstand. When he got back he sat down and unwrapped the package. He grinned and when I asked what the joke was he said, "You figured maybe I wouldn't come back."

I told him the idea hadn't occurred to me.

"I figured you were wondering if I was gonna just keep right on going and not come back. I'll admit I thought about it. For four months I've been thinking about that first fix when I got out. Last night one of the other guys says to me, 'Bobby, what's the first thing you're gonna do when you get out?' And I told him he already knew. Like I really wanted that shot. Some guys do their whole bit thinking about the girls they're gonna have when they get out. I just couldn't stop thinking about that first fix. But now, I don't know, I'm not thinkin' about it. I mean, like I'm thinkin' about it, but I haven't really wanted it. I don't know what it is, but I just don't want it. I wish Helen could feel that way. I wish I could *make* her feel that way. She really needs me and I guess that's one of the big reasons why I'm going out there. If I could help her get off stuff then that'd be one big thing—I guess the only big thing—that I've done in my life."

Two other waiting passengers walked by in front of us.

"I really feel funny in these clothes," Bobby said. "I feel like everyone's looking at me, like everyone knows where I just came from."

"No one's looking at you Bobby. Anyway, we'll get you some clothes when we get to Detroit. We'll go see Helen for a minute tonight and then you can see the doctor in the morning. I have to get a five-o'clock plane back tomorrow afternoon. The doctor wants to see you and Helen separately and he thought he'd like to see you first, okay?"

"Okay. You're the boss."

"No, Bobby, you're the boss. You don't have to go. If you want to go back to Needle Park now, you can."

He grinned again. "No, man. I ain't *ever* going back there. Because that would be nothin' but a hotshot for sure. For *sure*."

Chapter 20

We landed in Detroit, rented a car, and drove to Helen's motel. During the flight Bobby had grown more and more nervous. He wouldn't talk, and when the stewardess asked him to fasten his seat belt she had to say it three times before he heard her.

In the car he told me he thought maybe he wanted to spend the night with Helen and ask her what she thought about seeing the doctor and then if she liked the idea he would go with her. I tried to explain that as he had mentioned in the coffee shop earlier it might not be good for him to go back with Helen, that maybe after the doctor had seen them both he might suggest that they break up for a while. He didn't answer.

I expected an argument from Helen when I suggested that Bobby come with me to another motel and then visit the doctor in the morning without her. But she surprised me. When he walked through the door of her motel room she threw her arms around him and the first words out of her mouth were, "When are you going to see the doctor?"

She had put on a lot of weight—a good sign that she wasn't using heavily—and the room showed no visible signs that she had been taking off in it.

Bobby tried to sound authoritative. "I'm seeing him tomorrow. I'm going to stay tonight alone. I'll call you tomorrow after I see him." A look of surprise just barely flickered across her face, and she glanced at me. Then she brightened.

"That's fine. Then you'd better run, 'cause you'll want to be in good shape when you see him."

She started toward the bathroom. "Before you go I want to tell you something. Come here a second." Bobby followed her into the bathroom and she closed the door. In two minutes they were out again. Helen looked at me. "Just a little personal business," she said. "Take care of him."

Bobby and I went to another motel and got rooms that were next door but not connecting. Bobby laughed about that—the first time he had laughed since we left New York —and said that if he suddenly decided to cut out in the middle of the night I'd never know it. We sat in his room for a while and he began to talk.

"I'll tell you, at this point I really don't know if I can make it." He was very solemn, talking softly, more to himself than to me.

"I really don't know. I mean, I really don't think I *can* make it. Like just now, back there with Helen, I got very, very nervous. I really wanted to get off, real bad. Like it was the first time since I got out that I really wanted to get off. Since I got out—I make it sound like it was a year or something. It was only this morning. But anyway that's the longest I've ever been on the street without junk, I mean after coming out of jail, since the first time I ever went to jail. I mean, you'd think that after being away for four months the first thing I'd think of would be my girl, would be Helen, but with her today, as much as I missed her, all I could think of was junk and getting off."

"Did she give you anything in the bathroom?"

"You mean junk? No. But she had some. She said she had some."

"What did she give you?"

He reached in his pocket and threw a set of works on the bed.

"She said she wanted me to keep this for her."

"Why do you think she did that?"

"I don't know. She just wanted me to keep it. Maybe she's afraid of getting busted with it. I mean, she's not really hooked again, but she's chipping, I guess, and so probably she was afraid of getting busted with them."

"Maybe you should throw them away. If you want to be clean, that's a bad way to start."

He was silent for five minutes.

"It *is* a bad way, I mean just having those things around is no good, I know that, but I couldn't throw them away 'cause she said to keep them for her and they're probably the only set she's got and she'd tear me up if I threw them away."

Chapter 21

The doctor lived in an immense, sprawling old house that needed paint, plus a few things nailed back on here and there. He had a wife, four girls from four to ten, and two noisy German shepherds who did everything they could to keep us out, then jumped all over us when we got in.

"Sit down a second," the doctor said. "Ginny and I were just about to hitch up the team." We sat on the front porch and the doctor and his youngest daughter dragged a cart out of the back yard and began to hitch it to one of the dogs. The whole house—children yelling, dogs barking— was bedlam, and that seemed to relieve Bobby, since it drew attention away from him. The other dog came bouncing up onto the porch and put his front paws on Bobby's lap. Bobby patted him, and scratched his ear.

The cart was hitched and Ginny got in. The dog pulled her down to the corner, with the doctor trotting alongside. She got out and one of her sisters rode the cart back to the house. Another passenger got in—a little boy from the neighborhood who had been watching enviously—and the doctor called to Bobby.

"Come on, Bobby, run it down to the corner."

Bobby shook his head.

"I've gotta carve the dinner, Bobby, and the kids can't ride it alone. Just take it down to the corner and back. I'll be right back out."

Bobby blushed. With all the strangers looking at him it was easier to agree than to refuse. He got up and lifted the boy into the cart and walked down to the corner. He turned it around and sent it back, but he stayed on the corner. He looked up and down the block that ran perpendicular to the one the Doctor's house was on, and then started walking up the sidewalk, away from the house. He went about twenty feet, bent over as if to pick something up, and then came back to the house.

Eight of us were at the table for dinner, and the ordeal was one of great embarrassment for Bobby. These were more squares than he had ever been with at one time before, and the situation—a family Sunday dinner—was the squarest he had ever encountered. He must have wanted a fix very, very bad. After dinner the doctor did some magic tricks, and as the children watched and laughed Bobby sat in a chair in a corner of the living room and played with the dog that had put its paws in his lap on the porch.

We were getting ready to leave when the doctor called me into his library.

"He's very frightened but I might be able to work with him. I'm going to give him some tests and if they work out I'd like him to live here. Today he made friends with the dog. Tomorrow he'll be talking to Ginny. Eventually he'll learn to relate to the other children and then a few square adults. Then I'll get him a job and a place of his own to live. He'll come along. Tell me where he's staying and I'll get him over here again tomorrow. And I want to see his girlfriend. I'll probably want to break that up."

We left and drove to Helen's motel. On the way Bobby asked me what I had thought when he stayed down on the corner and started to walk up the block. He said he thought I would probably think he was running away. "Do you know what I was really doing?" he asked. "I threw away the works. Into the sewer."

Helen was lying on the bed nodding. A cooker was on the nighttable. When we came in she stood up and tried to come out of the nod.

"Gee, it's good you came over. I was up late last night and I've been asleep all day. If you hadn't come over I'd have slept the whole day away. How was the doc?"

"Okay," Bobby said. His eyes were on the cooker.

"He's going to come by tomorrow and pick Bobby up. He wants to give him some tests."

"Some tests!" she said. "Oh, boy. They going to test

you, Bobby? Not me. They wanted to do that to me in KY and I told them to go to hell. Wires all stuck in your head and everything like that. Not me. I saw a girl in KY they did that to." She shook her head gravely. "But that doesn't matter, Bobby. The doctor knows what's best. You should do what he says. And you'll love Detroit, Bobby. I know you will."

She put her arms around him and sat him down on the bed. "You remember Mickey, how he used to make you laugh with the stories about when he was in Sing Sing and he kept the bulls running around? Well, you're going to meet this guy here named Ricky who is just like him, only funnier. He's a great guy. I told him to come over tomorrow and help us move. He says he can get us a room in his hotel. It's a real swinging place. You'll love it, Bobby, and you'll love these people, too. They're real good stand-up people." She was beside him on the bed, nuzzling his neck. The cooker was two feet away from him and he could not keep his eyes off it.

"And there's this friend of Ricky's, his name is Frankie and he knows like every cop there is. I mean, it's not like New York here, baby—you got to know The Man and if you do you're in. And Frankie is *in*, baby, I'm here to tell you he is *in*."

She looked up at me. "What time is your plane? Bobby and I have some . . . some business we've been putting off for a long time . . . for four months." She touched the back of his neck.

"Don't look like that," she said to me. "I'm talking about love, not junk."

Her anger embarrassed Bobby. "Come on, Helen," he said. "Don't be like that. He knows what you're talking about."

I went to the door and opened it. They were still sitting on the bed and Helen had Bobby in her arms. She looked at me over his shoulder and smiled. It was the doctor, his wife, his children, and his dogs—versus heroin. She bit Bobby's ear and smiled at him. Bobby smiled back and put an arm around her shoulders.

Why must it be so—that junkies like Bob and Helen find it so impossible to free themselves of their habit? After all, heroin itself—looked at simply as a chemical—is not really all that bad for you. In fact, if you smoke a pack a day, drink a little too much, weigh more than you should, or even if you just have a bad cold, your system is taking a bigger beating than it would from heroin. Even a long-time, hard-core heroin addict, if he stops using the drug, say in a hospital or jail, loses all physical need for it within three to five days—less time than it takes to shake off a common cold. After that time, his body is clinically un-aware that it has ever had a shot. And even though the addict might be in miserable physical condition, his afflictions are caused not by heroin itself but by unsterile needles, impurities in the heroin he has used, and by his general neglect of his body. If he stays in the hospital for months of treatment and general drug-free routine he will walk out strong and healthy, completely cured of his *physical* addiction. But what is the first thing junkies do when they get out of a hospital? They take another shot. They head back to heroin as fast as buses, planes, and trains can get them to New York.

So addiction isn't really a physical problem at all. It's an emotional problem. The junkie is convinced that he has been thrown into life's conflicts without the armor and weapons that everybody else has. Heroin lets him escape the uneven battle. It deadens his desire for wealth, strength, success, sex—even for food. With heroin, he needs nothing more. The satisfactions sought so relentlessly by the rest of the world, the addict gets—temporarily—with a $5 deck of heroin. So he takes a shot.

But in exchange for these brief periods of artificial bliss he surrenders everything else. Whenever the junkie comes out of a high he faces the agonizing truth that his family, home, friends, and job are gone, his clothes are dirty, his neglected body is filthy and sick. Shame overwhelms him —and at that moment he may want desperately to stay off drugs. But heroin can handle shame, too. So he takes another shot.

Many who argue that the addict's problems are created not by drugs but by the attempts to deprive him of them go on to claim that if every addict could get drugs without resorting to crime, he might straighten up, take the time to sterilize needles, eat occasionally, maybe even work.

The best answer to this argument is to take a backward look: until fifty years ago, narcotics were completely legal in the United States. Opium in its various derivatives—today they include heroin, morphine, Dilaudid, and codeine —were basic ingredients in countless patent medicines. Many doctors and pharmacists handled narcotic drugs with the cure-all enthusiasm of an Army corpsman passing out aspirin. At the turn of this century one in every four hundred Americans was addicted to opium in one form or another. Many of them were unwittingly hooked on such accepted household nostrums as Mrs. Winslow's Soothing Syrup and Dr. Cole's Catarrh Cure.

Then, in 1914, Congress passed the Harrison Narcotics Act, forbidding anyone but licensed doctors to prescribe cocaine or opiates and then only "in the course of his professional practice." Five years later the Supreme Court ruled that professional practice did *not* include handing out narcotics for the sole purpose of satisfying addiction. All over the country, doctors cut off the flow of drugs, and addicts by the tens of thousands showed up at local boards of health for help. Government narcotics agents suggested drug-dispensing clinics as an answer, and some forty-four were set up by local authorities.

On the whole, the clinics appeared to have had no other purpose than to save addicts from exploitation by pushers. But there was a fatal flaw in this seemingly enlightened

program. Given an unlimited supply of heroin, few—if any
—addicts level off at a stable dose; an addict receiving a
prescribed amount from a clinic or doctor soon demands
more. To get it, he returns to the illegal pusher—and he is
back where he started.

After three years of experiment the clinics closed down,
largely on the advice of the medical profession. And the
American Medical Association today sticks by its opinion,
first expressed in clinic days: "Any method of treatment
for narcotic drug addiction, whether private, institutional,
official or governmental, which permits the addicted person
to dose himself with the habit-forming narcotic drugs
placed in his hands for self-administration is an unsatisfac-
tory treatment of addiction, begets deceptions, extends the
abuse of habit-forming narcotic drugs, and causes an in-
crease in crime."

But why limit the addict's dose at all? Why not give him
all he wants? First, it is not done because society—especially
the medical profession—feels a responsibility to cure the
sick, not just to abandon them to their sickness. And second, it is not done because if narcotics were legally available to everyone without prescription, addiction would
spread. A psychiatrist who has worked closely with addicts
for years points out that addiction is "pathological behavior
which can be viewed as infectious. The individual who is
susceptible to this particular disorder most often decides to
try drugs after his curiosity has been stimulated by the pres-
ence of an addict in the neighborhood."

A study by doctors at the federal narcotics hospital at

Lexington, Kentucky, indicates that in his lifetime the average addict introduces four nonusers to heroin. If addicts could get drugs legally, cheaply, and in unlimited quantity, they would hardly be less inclined to share them with nonusers than they are today. People who accepted heroin as a means of escaping their emotional problems *would* become addicted. The number of these addiction-prone individuals is enormous—perhaps a majority of the millions of people who are emotionally unequipped to tolerate discomfort, or who are directed toward pleasure more than responsibility.

Federal narcotics laws have been refined and tightened—often at the urging of the medical profession—since the Harrison Act, but they still permit much more freedom than most doctors realize, or are willing to exercise. "It is clear," says the Medical Society of the County of New York, "that the majority of physicians do not understand what kind of therapy they can undertake."

The laws do not, for example, forbid that a physician treat an addict or give him narcotics. They state only that he must do so in an effort to cure the addict, not simply to maintain his addiction, and that the doctor must not trust the addict to administer the drugs to himself. The laws require that treatment of an addict, during which drugs are given to reduce withdrawal discomfort, must—except in certain extreme circumstances—be restricted to a hospital. The doctor is permitted to dispense narcotics continuously to patients with painful chronic diseases and also to the "aged and infirm," whose collapse and death might result from withdrawal of the drug. When an addict is awaiting admittance for hospital treatment, a doctor may, for as long as two weeks, give him daily doses of a narcotic to hold off withdrawal. Also, restrictions on the use of narcotics may be modified for the benefit of research into addiction. In rare instances, it is even possible to secure government permission to maintain a young, otherwise healthy addict on drugs.

One reputable East Coast doctor, an exception in that he has treated many addicts, encountered a patient he thought could benefit from a steady, easily obtained supply of narcotics. The doctor had good reasons for his belief. Though numerous attempts to cure the patient had failed, he *did* have—and this was the crucial factor—an understanding and sympathetic family, eager to help him control his habit as much as possible. The doctor called the Federal Narcotics Bureau to explain the situation, and the Bureau agreed. The doctor then informed a pharmacy of the dosage the addict was authorized to receive. The pharmacist confirmed the legality of the procedure with his own call to the Bureau. The patient got his drugs.

But most doctors, although they publicly may advocate less stringent narcotics laws, privately want nothing to do with treating addicts, even within the framework of existing laws. Addicts make very bad patients. They often steal, lie, refuse to cooperate, and, when it comes to paying for anything except drugs, they're always broke. They can be withdrawn from drugs temporarily, but they almost always relapse. Give drugs to one and he returns the next day at the head of a long line of other hopeful addicts.

Some unscrupulous doctors take advantage of this very weakness. Without checking with the Federal Narcotics Bureau, or with other doctors, or with anyone, they deal with addicts strictly for the money they can make by writing illegal prescriptions.

Doctors—respectable and otherwise—will themselves sometimes turn to drugs. Exhausted by long hours, upset by personal problems, a doctor may be tempted to seek relief with a handy dose of morphine, Demerol, or Dilaudid. He unwisely assumes that he is not addiction-prone and that one shot will not necessarily lead to another. But doctors are not that different from other people—some of them do have an emotional susceptibility to addiction, and some of them do become addicted. One study indicated that the proportion of addicted doctors in the nation's total number of addicts was eight times the proportion of doctors in the general population—a concrete and disturbing example of what can happen when drugs are easily available.

Other examples of the dangers of an unlimited supply of drugs are evident abroad. Israel for four years operated drug clinics, but closed them when they failed to control the spread of addiction. The people of Denmark, where drugs are legal, consume 60 percent more drugs per capita than any other country in the world, and that government is now tightening controls.

But what of England? Almost everyone has heard of the "British system" of dispensing drugs to addicts. Over a period of years ill-informed commentators have created the impression that in Britain the addict invariably is treated as a sick person, in America as a criminal; that in Britain laws radically different from our own require the official registration of addicts, who may obtain their needed drugs simply by visiting a pharmacy and displaying their registration card. This "system," some observers have argued, has reduced the British narcotics problem to practically nothing.

British doctors and government officials are the first to deny that they have a system at all. Addicts there are not required to register, do not have registration cards, and cannot get drugs from a pharmacy without a doctor's prescription—though prescriptions are more easily obtained than in this country. A recent report by Britain's Lord Brain Committee states that that country's approach to drug abuse has been ineffective in controlling the number of addicts.

England has never had a severe narcotics problem; its procedure for handling addicts appears to be the result of the problem's small size, not the cause of it. The New York County Medical Society supports this conclusion. "There is no evidence," it says, "that the permissive approach in England is responsible for their low addiction rate. Other countries, such as Norway, with a similar approach, have very high addiction rates."

The British narcotics laws differ from our own in only one significant respect. A British doctor is allowed to dispense drugs to an addict if "it has been demonstrated that the patient, while capable of leading a useful and normal life when a certain dose is regularly administered, becomes incapable of this when the drug is entirely discontinued."

An infinitesimal number of addicts fall into this category. British journalists and researchers report that the problem there is far more acute than official statistics indicate, that there are perhaps four times as many addicts as the government admits—almost none of whom fulfill the "useful and normal life" requirement. Many of these addicts get their drugs from illegal pushers, from unscrupulous doctors who make a living writing "scripts" for addicts, or from other addicts who con more drugs from legitimate doctors than they really need.

A British doctor who studied thirty addicts seeking hospital treatment in 1962 reported that the going black-market price for heroin was 30 shillings ($4.20) per grain, about four times what a New York addict pays for it—an indication that British addicts sometimes find it tougher than Americans to get drugs. Like addicts in the United States, most of the thirty were thin, poorly dressed, dirty, and unemployed. On the whole, their lives—and the lives of other British addicts investigated more recently—appeared hardly less distressing than the life of the typical American big-city junkie.

Even if the British did have a system that could reduce their drug problem, would it be equally effective everywhere else? Since addiction is an emotional problem, an anti-addiction program that worked well in the British environment might not work so well on a people with a different emotional and cultural make-up. In support of this view, authorities point to the drug problem in Hong Kong. Although it is a British colony, with the opportunity of benefiting from the "British system," Hong Kong, with one third the population of New York City, has more addicts (approximately 150,000—or one for every ten adult males) than the entire United States. It is, in fact, the only city in the world with more heroin addicts than New York.

Even as practiced in England, the "British system" contains curious inconsistencies. Doctors there often accommodate heroin addicts by prescribing cocaine with their heroin—not because the addict needs cocaine, but because the two drugs mixed together provide a more pleasurable high than heroin alone. But, because cocaine is a far more dangerous drug than heroin—it may destroy brain cells and body tissues, induce paranoia and sometimes lead to violence—addicts would be better off without it. Marijuana, on the other hand, though far less dangerous, is totally illegal and strictly controlled in England.

Britain is not the only country where these two drugs are misunderstood. Some Americans—mostly members of beatnik groups—have protested that marijuana should be legalized, since it is not addicting. They are correct that it is not addicting (though it *is* strongly habituating), but they are wrong in assuming that this fact alone makes it safe. Many drugs which are not addicting are nevertheless dangerous, and quite properly controlled by law. (Cocaine, for example, is not physically addicting, but it *is* extremely dangerous.) Marijuana, in its action on the central nervous system, may produce dangerous and unpredictable effects ranging from distortions of time and space to hyperexhilaration and acute depression. Though many marijuana smokers never progress to heroin, a significant number do. Rarely is a heroin user found who did not come to the drug by way of marijuana.

Public confusion concerning which drugs are dangerous and which are not extends beyond the better-known narcotics like heroin. Newspaper stories of crimes committed by "drug addicts" rarely mention the specific drug. Because to most laymen, "drug addict" means heroin addict, the implication is that the crime was committed by someone on heroin. In the case of assaults or sex crimes, this is rarely true, unless the assailant was unusually desperate or had been using the drug in small doses or for a short time. The drugs that are more likely to produce violence are cocaine; amphetamines like Dexedrine, Benzedrine, Desoxyn; barbiturates like Tuinal, Seconal, Nembutal, when taken to great excess; and Doriden (thought to be responsible for much addict violence, it is often taken by heroin addicts when they cannot get heroin).

If opening the narcotics gate completely is not the answer to the problem, what about really locking it shut? Presumably, you cannot have drug addicts if you do not have drugs. The addict, deprived permanently of his supply, would not, according to most doctors, be likely to slip into some worse antisocial pursuit. He would perhaps have more than ordinary trouble keeping up on his rent payments, getting along with co-workers, coping with his family, handling routinely difficult problems of everyday life—the same symptoms displayed by nonaddicts with a personality disorder. But most authorities concede he would be decidedly better off than he is on heroin.

It appears that junkies in their struggle to be free of drugs have only one effective ally—time. Statistics indicate that as an addict grows older, he also grows up—the compulsion to avoid the hassle and degradation of a drug life overcomes his compulsion to use drugs, and he quits. This so-called "maturing out" theory is held by many of the doctors at Lexington. They point out that half the country's addicts are in their twenties, only 11 percent are over forty. Where are all the older junkies? The hope is that many of them have aged into abstinence and are leading reasonably normal lives—not knowing and not caring when the next panic will begin.